MEI STRUCTURED MATHEMATICS

THIRD EDITION

Mechanics 3

Pat Bryden
with
John Berry
Ted Graham
Roger Porkess

Series Editor: Roger Porkess

Hodder Murray

A MEMBER OF THE HODDER HEADLINE GROUP

The Publishers would like to thank the following for permission to reproduce copyright material:
Photo credits NASA/Roger Ressmeyer/CORBIS (page 1); Kevin R. Morris/CORBIS (page 1); Tim Wright/CORBIS (page 1); Reuters New Media Inc/CORBIS (page 15); Hodder Picture Library (page 38); Kate Fullerty (page 51 both); Emma Lee/Life File (pages 63, 67, 82 right and 144 left); Nick Nicholson/Hawkley Studios (page 67); Matthew Mendelsohn/CORBIS (page 82 top left); Gary Braasch/CORBIS (page 82 bottom left); Andrew Ward/Life File (pages 112 and 132 right); The Genius of China, photographer unknown (page 132 left); Adam Hart-Davies/Science Photo Library (page 141); Pat Bryden (page 142); The Craft of the Potter, photographer unknown (page 143); Jane Burton/Bruce Coleman Collection (page 144 right).

Acknowledgements
OCR accept no responsibility whatsoever for the accuracy or method of working in the answers given.

Every effort has been made to trace all copyright holders, but if any have been inadvertently overlooked the Publishers will be pleased to make the necessary arrangements at the first opportunity.

Although every effort has been made to ensure that website addresses are correct at time of going to press, Hodder Murray cannot be held responsible for the content of any website mentioned in this book. It is sometimes possible to find a relocated web page by typing in the address of the home page for a website in the URL window of your browser.

Hodder Headline's policy is to use papers that are natural, renewable and recyclable products and made from wood grown in sustainable forests. The logging and manufacturing processes are expected to conform to the environmental regulations of the country of origin.

Orders: please contact Bookpoint Ltd, 130 Milton Park, Abingdon, Oxon OX14 4SB. Telephone: (44) 01235 827720. Fax: (44) 01235 400454. Lines are open 9 am to 6 pm, Monday to Saturday, with a 24-hour message-answering service. Visit our website at www.hoddereducation.co.uk

© J. Berry, P. Bryden, E. Graham, R. Porkess 2005
First Edition published in 1995
Second Edition published in 2000
Third Edition published in 2005 by
Hodder Murray, an imprint of Hodder Education,
a member of the Hodder Headline Group
338 Euston Road
London NW1 3BH

Impression number   10 9 8 7 6 5 4 3 2 1
Year 2010 2009 2008 2007 2006 2005

Typeset in 10.5/14 pt Minion by Tech-Set, Gateshead, Tyne & Wear.
Printed and bound in Great Britain by Martins the Printers, Berwick-upon-Tweed

A catalogue record for this title is available from the British Library

ISBN-10: 0340 889977
ISBN-13: 978 0340 889978

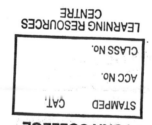

MEI Structured Mathematics

Mathematics is not only a beautiful and exciting subject in its own right but also one that underpins many other branches of learning. It is consequently fundamental to the success of a modern economy.

MEI Structured Mathematics is designed to increase substantially the number of people taking the subject post-GCSE, by making it accessible, interesting and relevant to a wide range of students.

It is a credit accumulation scheme based on 45 hour units which may be taken individually or aggregated to give Advanced Subsidiary (AS) and Advanced GCE (A Level) qualifications in Mathematics and Further Mathematics. The units may also be used to obtain credit towards other types of qualification.

The course is examined by OCR (previously the Oxford and Cambridge Schools Examination Board) with examinations held in January and June each year.

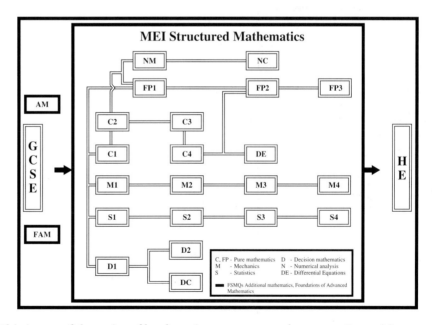

This is one of the series of books written to support the course. Its position within the whole scheme can be seen in the diagram above.

Mathematics in Education and Industry (MEI) is an independent curriculum development body which aims to promote links between education and industry in mathematics. MEI produce relevant examination specifications at GCSE, AS and A Level (including Further Mathematics) and for Free Standing Mathematics Qualifications (FSMQs); these are examined by OCR.

In partnership with Hodder Murray, MEI are responsible for three major series of textbooks: Formula One Maths for Key Stage 3, Hodder Mathematics for GCSE and the MEI Structured Mathematics series, including this book, for AS and A Level.

As well as textbooks, MEI take a leading role in the development of on-line resources to support mathematics. The books in this series are complemented by a major MEI website providing full solutions to the exercises, extra questions including on-line multiple choice tests, interactive demonstrations of the mathematics, schemes of work, and much more.

In recent years MEI have worked hard to promote Further Mathematics and, in conjunction with the DfES, they are now establishing the national network of Further Mathematics Centres.

MEI are committed to supporting the professional development of teachers. In addition to a programme of Continual Professional Development, MEI, in partnership with several universities, co-ordinate the Teaching Advanced Mathematics programme, a course designed to give teachers the skills and confidence to teach A Level mathematics successfully.

Much of the work of MEI is supported by the Gatsby Charitable Foundation.

MEI is a registered charity and a charitable company.

MEI's website and email addresses are www.mei.org.uk and office@mei.org.uk.

Introduction

This is the third in the series of books written to support the Mechanics modules of MEI Structured Mathematics, but you may also use them for an independent course of study in the subject. For those who take an A level consisting of pure mathematics and mechanics only, this book marks the start of the mechanics in Further Mathematics.

In the past, mechanics has often been presented as algebraic manipulation with little reference to the real world. The books in this series have been designed to present the subject as a powerful and exciting means of modelling real situations. The many applications of mechanics make it an important subject for applied mathematicians, scientists and engineers, but to use mechanics on real problems you must also understand the whole modelling procedure, which allows you to relate your knowledge of mathematics to the world around you. These books help you to do this.

In *Mechanics 3* you meet circular motion, elasticity and simple harmonic motion for the first time, and use calculus methods to extend earlier work on centre of mass. The book, and the basic mechanics course, is completed by the final chapter on dimensional analysis.

This is the third edition of this book and thanks are due to Pat Bryden for her work in preparing it. In this edition the material has been updated and many recent examination questions have been included. We would also like to thank our copy editor Penny Nicholson and the many people who have given help and advice with this book as it has developed, and also the various examination boards who have allowed us to use their questions in the exercises.

Readers who are interested in a possible career in mathematics may wish to visit *www.mathscareers.org.uk*.

Pat Bryden, Roger Porkess, John Berry and Ted Graham

Key to symbols in this book

?   This symbol means that you may want to discuss a point with your teacher. If you are working on your own there are answers in the back of the book. It is important, however, that you have a go at answering the questions before looking up the answers if you are to understand the mathematics fully.

⚠   This is a warning sign. It is used where a common mistake, misunderstanding or tricky point is being described.

      This is the ICT icon. It indicates where you should use a graphic calculator or a computer.

e   This symbol and a dotted line down the right-hand side of the page indicates material which is beyond the criteria for the unit but which is included for completeness.

      Harder questions are indicated with stars. Many of these go beyond the usual examination standard.

Contents

1

Circular motion

Whirlpools and storms his circling arm invest
With all the might of gravitation blest.

Alexander Pope

These pictures show some objects which move in circular paths. What other examples can you think of?

❓ What makes objects move in circles?

Why does the moon circle the earth?

What happens to the 'hammer' when the athlete lets it go?

Does the pilot of the plane need to be strapped into his seat at the top of a loop in order not to fall out?

The answers to these questions lie in the nature of circular motion. Even if an object is moving at constant speed in a circle, its velocity keeps changing because its direction of motion keeps changing. Consequently the object is accelerating and so, according to Newton's first law, there must be a force acting on it. The force required to keep an object moving in a circle can be provided in many ways.

Without the earth's gravitational force, the moon would move off at constant speed in a straight line into space. The wire attached to the athlete's hammer provides a tension force which keeps the ball moving in a circle. When the athlete lets go, the ball flies off at a tangent because the tension has disappeared.

Although it would be sensible for the pilot to be strapped in, no upward force is necessary to stop him falling out of the plane because his weight contributes to the force required for motion in a circle.

In this chapter, these effects are explained.

Notation

To describe circular motion (or indeed any other topic) mathematically you need a suitable notation. It will be helpful in this chapter to use the notation (attributed to Newton) for differentiation with respect to time in which, for example, $\dfrac{ds}{dt}$ is written as $\dot{s}$, and $\dfrac{d^2\theta}{dt^2}$ as $\ddot{\theta}$.

Figure 1.1 shows a particle P moving round the circumference of a circle of radius r, centre O. At time t, the position vector $\overrightarrow{OP}$ of the particle makes an angle θ (in radians) with the fixed direction $\overrightarrow{OA}$. The arc length AP is denoted by s.

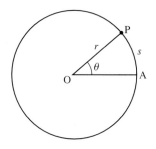

Figure 1.1

Angular speed

Using this notation,

$$s = r\theta$$

Differentiating this with respect to time using the product rule gives:

$$\frac{ds}{dt} = r\frac{d\theta}{dt} + \theta\frac{dr}{dt}.$$

Since r is constant for a circle, $\dfrac{dr}{dt} = 0$, so the rate at which the arc length increases is:

$$\frac{ds}{dt} = r\frac{d\theta}{dt} \qquad \text{or} \qquad \dot{s} = r\dot{\theta}. \qquad \qquad ①$$

In this equation $\dot{s}$ is the speed at which P is moving round the circle (often denoted by v), and $\dot{\theta}$ is the rate at which the angle θ is increasing, i.e. the rate at which the position vector $\overrightarrow{OP}$ is rotating.

The quantity $\dfrac{d\theta}{dt}$, or $\dot{\theta}$, can be called the *angular velocity* or the *angular speed* of P. In more advanced work, angular velocity is treated as a vector, whose direction is taken to be that of the axis of rotation. In this book, $\dfrac{d\theta}{dt}$ is often referred to as angular speed, but is given a sign: positive when θ is increasing (usually anticlockwise) and negative when θ is decreasing (usually clockwise).

Angular speed is often denoted by ω, the Greek letter omega. So the equation $\dot{s} = r\dot{\theta}$ may be written as

$$v = r\omega.$$

Notice that for this equation to hold, θ must be measured in radians, so the angular speed is measured in *radians per second* or rad s^{-1}.

? Angular speeds are often written as multiples of π unless otherwise requested. Why is this?

Figure 1.2 shows a disc rotating about its centre, O, with angular speed ω. The line OP represents any radius.

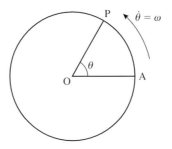

Figure 1.2

Every point on the disc describes a circular path, and all points have the same angular speed. However the *actual* speed of any point depends on its distance from the centre: increasing r in the equation $v = r\omega$ increases v. You will appreciate this if you have ever been at the end of a rotating line of people in a dance or watched a body of marching soldiers wheeling round a corner.

Angular speeds are sometimes measured in revolutions per second or revolutions per minute (rpm) where one revolution is equal to 2π radians. For example, turntables for vinyl records rotate at 45 or $33\frac{1}{3}$ rpm while a computer hard disc might spin at 7200 rpm or more. At cruising speeds, crankshafts in car engines typically rotate at 3000 to 4000 rpm.

EXAMPLE 1.1

A police car drives at 40 mph around a roundabout in a circle of radius 16 m. A second car moves so that it has the same angular speed as the police car but in a circle of radius 12 m. Is the second car breaking the 30 mph speed limit? (Use the approximation 1 mile $= \frac{8}{5}$ km.)

SOLUTION

Converting miles per hour to metres per second gives:

$$40 \text{ mph} = 40 \times \tfrac{8}{5} \text{ km h}^{-1}$$

$$= \frac{40 \times 8 \times 1000}{5 \times 3600} \text{ ms}^{-1}$$

$$= \frac{160}{9} \text{ ms}^{-1}$$

Using $v = r\omega$,

$$\omega = \frac{160}{9 \times 16} \text{ in rad s}^{-1}$$

$$= \frac{10}{9} \text{ in rad s}^{-1}$$

The speed of the second car is:

$$v = 12\omega$$

$$= \frac{10}{9} \times 12 \text{ in ms}^{-1}$$

$$= \frac{120 \times 5 \times 3600}{9 \times 8 \times 1000} \text{ in mph}$$

$$= 30 \text{ mph}$$

The second car is just on the speed limit.

Notes

1 Notice that working in fractions gives an exact answer.

2 A quicker way to do this question would be to notice that, because the cars have the same angular speed, the actual speeds of the cars are proportional to the radii of the circles in which they are moving. Using this method it is possible to stay in mph. The ratio of the two radii is $\frac{12}{16}$ so the speed of the second car is $\frac{12}{16} \times 40 \text{ mph} = 30 \text{ mph}$.

EXERCISE 1A

1 Find the angular speed, in radians per second correct to one decimal place, of records rotating at

   (i) 78 rpm

   (ii) 45 rpm

   (iii) $33\frac{1}{3}$ rpm.

2 A flywheel is rotating at 300 rad s^{-1}. Express this angular speed in rpm, correct to the nearest whole number.

3 The London Eye observation wheel has a diameter of 135 m and completes one revolution in 30 minutes.
  (i) Calculate its angular speed in
    (a) rpm   (b) radians per second.
  (ii) Calculate the speed of the point on the circumference where passengers board the moving wheel.

4 A lawnmower engine is started by pulling a rope that has been wound round a cylinder of radius 4 cm. Find the angular speed of the cylinder at a moment when the rope is being pulled with a speed of 1.3 ms^{-1}. Give your answers in radians per second, correct to one decimal place.

5 The wheels of a car have radius 20 cm. What is the angular speed, in radians per second correct to one decimal place, of a wheel when the car is travelling at
  (i) 10 ms^{-1} (ii) 30 ms^{-1}?

6 The angular speed of an audio CD changes continuously so that a laser can read the data at a constant speed of 12 ms^{-1}. Find the angular speed (in rpm) when the distance of the laser from the centre is
  (i) 30 mm   (ii) 55 mm.

7 What is the average angular speed of the earth in radians per second as it
  (i) orbits the sun
  (ii) rotates about its own axis?

  The radius of the earth is 6400 km.
  (iii) At what speed is someone on the equator travelling relative to the centre of the earth?
  (iv) At what speed are you travelling relative to the centre of the earth?

8 A tractor has front wheels of diameter 70 cm and back wheels of diameter 1.6 m. What is the ratio of their angular speeds when the tractor is being driven along a straight road?

9 (i) Find the kinetic energy of a 50 kg person riding a big wheel with radius 5 m when the ride is rotating at 3 rpm. You should assume that the person can be modelled as a particle.
  (ii) Explain why this modelling assumption is necessary.

10 The minute hand of a clock is 1.2 m long and the hour hand is 0.8 m long.
  (i) Find the speeds of the tips of the hands.
  (ii) Find the ratio of the speeds of the tips of the hands and explain why this is not the same as the ratio of the angular speeds of the hands.

11 The diagram represents a 'Chairoplane' ride at a fair. It completes one revolution every 2.5 seconds.

(i) Find the radius of the circular path which a rider follows.

(ii) Find the speed of a rider.

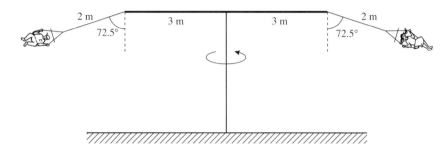

12 The position vector of a rider on a helter-skelter is given by

$$\mathbf{r} = 2\sin t\,\mathbf{i} + 2\cos t\,\mathbf{j} + (8 - \tfrac{1}{2}t)\mathbf{k}$$

where the units are in metres and seconds. The unit vector $\mathbf{k}$ is vertically upwards.

(i) Find an expression for the velocity of the rider at time t.

(ii) Find the speed of the rider at time t.

(iii) Find the magnitude and direction of the rider's acceleration when $t = \dfrac{\pi}{4}$.

13 The tape in a cassette player passes over the heads at a speed of $5\,\mathrm{cm\,s^{-1}}$ and is taken up on a spool of diameter 1.7 cm. The thickness of the tape is 0.01 mm. The take-up spool is initially empty. Find an expression for the angular speed of the take-up spool at time t seconds. What modelling assumptions have you made?

14 The diagram shows a roundabout in a playground, seen from above. It is rotating clockwise. A child on the roundabout at X, aims a ball at a friend sitting opposite at Y.

(i) Once the ball is thrown, can the friend catch it?

(ii) Draw a plan of the path of the ball after it has been thrown.

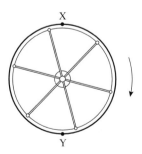

Velocity and acceleration

Velocity and acceleration are both vector quantities. They can be expressed either in magnitude–direction form, or in components. When describing circular motion or other orbits it is most convenient to take components in directions along the radius (*radial* direction) and at right angles to it (*transverse* direction).

For a particle moving round a circle of radius r, the velocity has:

radial component: 0

transverse component: $r\dot{\theta}$ or $r\omega$.

The acceleration of a particle moving round a circle of radius r has:

radial component: $-r\dot{\theta}^2$ or $-r\omega^2$

transverse component: $r\ddot{\theta}$ or $r\dot{\omega}$.

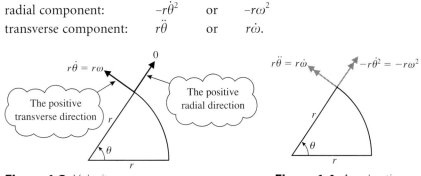

Figure 1.3 *Velocity*   **Figure 1.4** *Acceleration*

The transverse component is just what you would expect, the radius multiplied by the angular acceleration, $\ddot{\theta}$. If the particle has constant angular speed, its angular acceleration is zero and so the transverse component of its acceleration is also zero.

In contrast, the radial component of the acceleration, $-r\omega^2$, is almost certainly not a result you would have expected intuitively. It tells you that a particle travelling in a circle is always accelerating towards the centre of the circle, but without ever getting any closer to the centre. If this seems a strange idea, you may find it helpful to remember that circular motion is not a natural state; left to itself a particle will travel in a straight line. To keep a particle in the unnatural state of circular motion it must be given an acceleration at right angles to its motion, i.e. towards the centre of the circle.

The derivation of these expressions for the acceleration of a particle in circular motion is complicated by the fact that the radial and transverse directions are themselves changing as the particle moves round the circle, in contrast to the fixed x and y directions in the Cartesian system. The derivation is given on page 186 in the chapter entitled Mathematical notes. At first reading you may prefer to accept the results, but make sure that at a later stage you work through and understand the derivation.

Circular motion with constant speed

In this section, the circular motion is assumed to be uniform and so have no transverse component of acceleration. Later in the chapter (page 26 onwards), situations are considered in which the angular speed varies.

Problems involving circular motion often refer to the actual speed of the object, rather than its angular speed. It is easy to convert the one into the other using the relationship $v = r\omega$. This relationship can also be used to express the magnitude of the acceleration in terms of v and r.

$$\omega = \frac{v}{r}$$

$$a = r\omega^2 = r\left(\frac{v}{r}\right)^2$$

$$\Rightarrow \quad a = \frac{v^2}{r} \text{ towards the centre.}$$

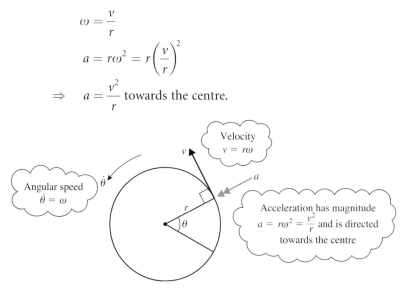

Figure 1.5

| EXAMPLE 1.2 |

A fly is standing on a record at a distance of 8 cm from the centre. If the record is rotating at 45 rpm, find

(i) the angular speed of the fly in radians per second
(ii) the speed of the fly in metres per second
(iii) the acceleration of the fly.

SOLUTION

(i) One revolution is 2π rad so

$$45 \text{ rpm} = 45 \times 2\pi \text{ rad min}^{-1}$$

$$= \frac{45 \times 2\pi}{60} \text{ rad s}^{-1}$$

$$= \frac{3\pi}{2} \text{ rad s}^{-1}.$$

(ii) If the speed of the fly is $v\,\text{ms}^{-1}$, v can be found using

$$v = r\omega$$

$$= 0.08 \times \frac{3\pi}{2}$$

$$= 0.377\ldots$$

So the speed of the fly is $0.38\,\text{ms}^{-1}$ (to 2 d.p.).

(iii) The acceleration of the fly is given by

$$r\omega^2 = 0.08 \times \left(\frac{3\pi}{2}\right)^2 \text{ms}^{-2}$$

$$= 1.78\,\text{ms}^{-2}.$$

It is directed towards the centre of the record.

 A wheel of radius r m is rolling in a straight line with forward speed $u\,\text{ms}^{-1}$. What are

(i) the speed of the point which is instantaneously in contact with the ground

(ii) the angular speed of the wheel

(iii) the velocities of the highest point and the point on the edge of the wheel which is level with and behind the axle?

The forces required for circular motion

Newton's first law of motion states that a body will continue in a state of rest or uniform motion in a straight line unless acted upon by an external force. Any object moving in a circle, such as the police car and the fly in Examples 1.1 and 1.2 must therefore be acted upon by a resultant force in order to produce the required acceleration towards the centre.

A force towards the centre is called a *centripetal* (centre-seeking) force. A resultant centripetal force is necessary for a particle to move in a circular path.

Examples of circular motion

You are now in a position to use Newton's second law to determine theoretical answers to some of the questions which were posed at the beginning of this chapter. These will, as usual, be obtained using models of the true motion which will be based on simplifying assumptions, for example zero air resistance. Large objects are assumed to be particles concentrated at their centres of mass.

EXAMPLE 1.3

A coin is placed on a rotating turntable. Its centre is 5 cm from the centre of rotation and the coefficient of friction, μ, between the coin and the turntable is 0.5.

(i) If the speed of rotation of the turntable is gradually increased, at what angular speed will the coin begin to slide?

(ii) What happens next?

SOLUTION

(i) Because the speed of the turntable is increased only gradually, it can be assumed that the coin will not slip tangentially.

Figure 1.6 shows the forces acting on the coin, and its acceleration.

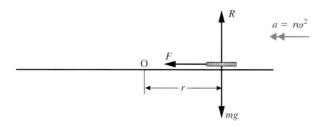

Figure 1.6

The acceleration is towards the centre, O, of the circular path so there must be a frictional force F in that direction.

There is no vertical component of acceleration, so the resultant force acting on the coin has no vertical component.

Therefore $R - mg = 0$

$$R = mg \qquad \text{①}$$

By Newton's second law towards the centre of the circle:

$$\text{Force } F = ma = mr\omega^2 \qquad \text{②}$$

The coin will not slide so long as $F \leqslant \mu R$.

Substituting from ② and ① this gives

$$mr\omega^2 \leqslant \mu mg$$
$$\Rightarrow \quad r\omega^2 \leqslant \mu g$$

Notice that the mass, m, has been eliminated at this stage, so that the answer does not depend upon it

Taking g in ms^{-2} as 9.8 and substituting $r = 0.05$ and $\mu = 0.5$

$$\omega^2 \leqslant 98$$
$$\omega \leqslant \sqrt{98}$$
$$\omega \leqslant 9.89 \ldots$$

The coin will move in a circle provided that the angular speed is less than about 10 rad s^{-1} and this speed is independent of the mass of the coin.

(ii) When the angular speed increases beyond this, the coin slips to a new position. If the angular speed continues to increase the coin will slip right off the turntable. When it reaches the edge it will fly off in the direction of the tangent.

The conical pendulum

A conical pendulum consists of a small bob tied to one end of a string. The other end of the string is fixed and the bob is made to rotate in a horizontal circle below the fixed point so that the string describes a cone as in figure 1.7.

Figure 1.7

EXPERIMENT

1 Draw a diagram showing the magnitude and direction of the acceleration of a bob and the forces acting on it.

2 In the case that the radius of the circle remains constant, try to predict the effect on the angular speed when the length of the string is increased or when the mass of the bob is increased. What might happen when the angular speed increases?

3 Draw two circles of equal diameter on horizontal surfaces so that two people can make the bobs of conical pendulums rotate in circles of the same radius.

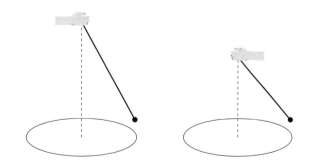

Figure 1.8

(i) Compare pendulums of different lengths with bobs of equal mass.

(ii) Compare pendulums of the same length but with bobs of different masses.

Does the angular speed depend on the length of the pendulum or the mass of the bob?

4 What happens when somebody makes the speed of the bob increase?

5 Can a bob be made to rotate with the string horizontal?

Theoretical model for the conical pendulum

A conical pendulum may be modelled as a particle of mass m attached to a light, inextensible string of length l. The mass is rotating in a horizontal circle with angular speed ω and the string makes an angle α with the downward vertical. The radius of the circle is r and the tension in the string is T, all in consistent units (e.g. S.I. units). The situation is shown in figure 1.9.

Figure 1.9

The magnitude of the acceleration is $r\omega^2$. The acceleration acts in a horizontal direction towards the centre of the circle. This means that there must be a resultant force acting towards the centre of the circle.

There are two forces acting on this particle, its weight mg and the tension T in the string.

As the acceleration of the particle has no vertical component, the resultant force has no vertical component, so

$$T\cos\alpha - mg = 0 \qquad \qquad ①$$

Using Newton's second law towards the centre, O, of the circle

$$T\sin\alpha = ma = mr\omega^2 \qquad \qquad ②$$

In triangle AOP $r = l\sin\alpha$

Substituting for r in ② gives $\quad T\sin\alpha = m(l\sin\alpha)\omega^2$

$$\Rightarrow \quad T = ml\omega^2$$

Substituting this in ① gives

$$ml\omega^2\cos\alpha - mg = 0$$

$$\Rightarrow \quad l\cos\alpha = \frac{g}{\omega^2} \qquad\qquad ③$$

This equation provides sufficient information to give theoretical answers to the questions in the experiment.

- When r is kept constant and the length of the string is increased, the length $AO = l\cos\alpha$ increases. Equation ③ indicates that the value of $\frac{g}{\omega^2}$ increases and so the angular speed ω decreases. Conversely, the angular speed increases when the string is shortened.
- The mass of the particle does not appear in equation ③, so it has no effect on the angular speed, ω.
- When the length of the pendulum is unchanged, but the angular speed is increased, $\cos\alpha$ decreases, leading to an increase in the angle α and hence in r.
- If $\alpha \geqslant 90°$, $\cos\alpha \leqslant 0$, so $\frac{g}{\omega^2} \leqslant 0$, which is impossible. You can see from figure 1.9 that the tension in the string must have a vertical component to balance the weight of the particle.

EXAMPLE 1.4

The diagram on the right represents one of several arms of a fairground ride, shown on the left. The arms rotate about an axis and riders sit in chairs linked to the arms by chains.

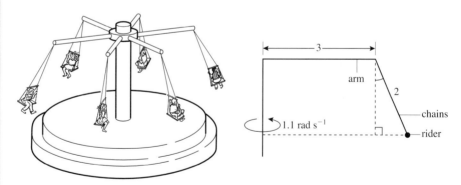

Figure 1.10

The chains are 2 m long and the arms are 3 m long. Find the angle that the chains make with the vertical when the rider rotates at $1.1\,\text{rad s}^{-1}$.

SOLUTION

Let T N be the resultant tension in the chains holding a chair, and m kg the mass of chair and rider.

Figure 1.11

If the chains make an angle α with the vertical, the motion is in a horizontal circle with radius given by

$$r = 3 + 2\sin\alpha.$$

The magnitude of the acceleration is given by

$$r\omega^2 = (3 + 2\sin\alpha)1.1^2.$$

It is in a horizontal direction towards the centre of the circle. Using Newton's second law in this direction gives

$$\text{Force} = mr\omega^2$$
$$\Rightarrow \quad T\sin\alpha = m(3 + 2\sin\alpha)1.1^2$$
$$= 1.21m(3 + 2\sin\alpha) \qquad \text{①}$$

Vertically $\qquad T\cos\alpha - mg = 0$

$$\Rightarrow \qquad T = \frac{mg}{\cos\alpha}$$

Substituting for T in equation ①:

$$\frac{mg}{\cos\alpha}\sin\alpha = 1.21m(3 + 2\sin\alpha)$$
$$\Rightarrow \quad 9.8\tan\alpha = 3.63 + 2.42\sin\alpha$$

Since m cancels out at this stage, the angle does not depend on the mass of the rider

This equation cannot be solved directly, but a numerical method will give you the solution $25.5°$ correct to three significant figures. You might like to solve the equation yourself or check that this solution does in fact satisfy the equation.

Note

Since the answer does not depend on the mass of the rider and chair, when riders of different masses, or even no riders, are on the equipment all the chains should make the same angle with the vertical.

Banked tracks

ACTIVITY

⚠ Keep away from other people and breakable objects when carrying out this activity.

Place a coin on a piece of stiff A4 card and hold it horizontally at arm's length with the coin near your hand.

Figure 1.12

Turn round slowly so that your hand moves in a horizontal circle. Now gradually speed up. The outcome will probably not surprise you.

What happens, though, if you tilt the card?

Figure 1.13

You may have noticed that when they curve round bends, most roads are banked so that the edge at the outside of the bend is slightly higher than that at the inside. For the same reason the outer rail of a railway track is slightly higher than the inner rail when it goes round a bend. On bobsleigh tracks the bends are almost bowl shaped, with a much greater gradient on the outside.

Figure 1.14 shows a car rounding a bend on a road which is banked so that the cross-section makes an angle α with the horizontal.

Figure 1.14

In modelling such situations, it is usual to treat the bend as part of a horizontal circle whose radius is large compared to the width of the car. In this case, the radius of the circle is taken to be r metres, and the speed of the car constant at v metres per second. The car is modelled as a particle which has an acceleration of $\dfrac{v^2}{r}$ ms^{-2} in a horizontal direction towards the centre of the circle. The forces and acceleration are shown in figure 1.15.

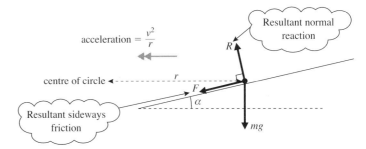

Figure 1.15

The direction of the frictional force F will be up or down the slope depending on whether the car has a tendency to slip sideways towards the inside or outside of the bend.

 Under what conditions do you think each of these will occur?

EXAMPLE 1.5

A car is rounding a bend of radius 100 m which is banked at an angle of 10° to the horizontal. At what speed must the car travel to ensure it has no tendency to slip sideways?

SOLUTION

When there is no tendency to slip there is no frictional force, so in the plane perpendicular to the direction of motion of the car, the forces and acceleration are as shown in figure 1.16. The only horizontal force is provided by the horizontal component of the normal reaction of the road on the car.

Figure 1.16

Vertically, there is no acceleration so there is no resultant force

$$Rcos10° - mg = 0$$

$$\Rightarrow \quad R = \frac{mg}{cos10°} \qquad \qquad ①$$

By Newton's second law in the horizontal direction towards the centre of the circle

$$Rsin10° = ma = \frac{mv^2}{r}$$

$$= \frac{mv^2}{100}$$

Substituting for R from ①

$$\left(\frac{mg}{cos10°}\right)sin10° = \frac{mv^2}{100}$$

$$\Rightarrow \quad v^2 = 100gtan10°$$

$$\Rightarrow \quad v = 13.15\ldots$$

The mass, m, cancels out at this stage, so the answer does not depend on it

The speed of the car must be about $13.15\,\text{ms}^{-1}$ or $30\,\text{mph}$.

There are two important points to notice in this example.

- The speed is the same whatever the mass of the car.
- The example looks at the situation when the car does not tend to slide, and finds the speed at which this is the case. At this speed the car does not depend on friction to keep it from sliding, and indeed it could travel safely round the bend at this speed even in very icy conditions. However, at other speeds there is a tendency to slide, and friction actually helps the car to follow its intended path.

Safe speeds on a bend

What would happen in the previous example if the car travelled either more slowly than $13.15\,\text{ms}^{-1}$ or more quickly?

The answer is that there would be a frictional force acting so as to prevent the car from sliding across the road.

There are two possible directions for the frictional force. When the vehicle is stationary or travelling slowly, there is a tendency to slide down the slope and the friction acts up the slope to prevent this. When it is travelling quickly round the bend, the car is more likely to slide up the slope, so the friction acts down the slope.

Fortunately, under most road conditions, the coefficient of friction between tyres and the road is large, typically about 0.8. This means that there is a range of speeds that are safe for negotiating any particular bend.

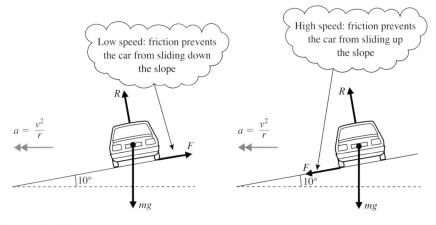

Figure 1.17

1 Using a particle model for the car, show that it will not slide up or down the slope provided

$$\sqrt{rg\frac{(\sin\alpha - \mu\cos\alpha)}{(\cos\alpha + \mu\sin\alpha)}} < v < \sqrt{rg\frac{(\sin\alpha + \mu\cos\alpha)}{(\cos\alpha - \mu\sin\alpha)}}$$

If $r = 100$ and $\alpha = 10°$ (so that $\tan\alpha = 0.176$) the minimum and maximum safe speeds (in mph) for different values of μ are given in the following table.

μ	0	0.1	0.2	0.3	0.4	0.5	0.6	0.7	0.8	0.9	1.0	1.1	1.2
Minimum safe speed	30	19	0	0	0	0	0	0	0	0	0	0	0
Maximum safe speed	30	37	44	50	55	61	66	70	75	80	84	89	93

2 Would you regard this bend as safe? How, by changing the values of r and α, could you make it safer?

EXAMPLE 1.6

A bend on a railway track has a radius of 500 m and is to be banked so that a train can negotiate it at 60 mph without the need for a lateral force between its wheels and the rail. The distance between the rails is 1.43 m.

How much higher should the outside rail be than the inside one?

SOLUTION

There is very little friction between the track and the wheels of a train. Any sideways force required is provided by the 'lateral thrust' between the wheels and the rail. The ideal speed for the bend is such that the lateral thrust is zero.

Figure 1.18 shows the forces acting on the train and its acceleration when the track is banked at an angle α to the horizontal.

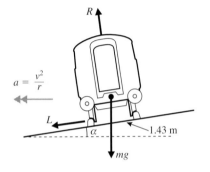

Figure 1.18

When there is no lateral thrust, $L = 0$.

Horizontally: $\qquad\qquad R\sin\alpha = \dfrac{mv^2}{r}$ ①

Vertically: $\qquad\qquad R\cos\alpha = mg$ ②

Dividing ① by ② gives $\qquad \tan\alpha = \dfrac{v^2}{rg}$

Using the fact that 60 mph $= 26.8\ \text{ms}^{-1}$ this becomes

$$\tan\alpha = 0.147$$
$$\Rightarrow \quad \alpha = 8.4° \text{ (to 2 s.f.)}$$

The outside rail should be raised by $1.43\sin\alpha$ metres, i.e. by about 21 cm.

1 The diagram shows two cars, A and B, travelling at constant speeds in different lanes (radii 24 m and 20 m) round a roundabout. Car A has speed $18\,\text{ms}^{-1}$ and car B has speed $15\,\text{ms}^{-1}$.

Answer the following questions, giving reasons for your answers.

(i) Which car has the greater angular speed?

(ii) Is one car overtaking the other?

(iii) Find the magnitude of the acceleration of each car.

(iv) In which direction is the resultant force on each car acting?

2 Two coins are placed on a horizontal turntable. Coin A has mass 15 g and is placed 5 cm from the centre; coin B has mass 10 g and is placed 7.5 cm from the centre. The coefficient of friction between each coin and the turntable is 0.4.

(i) Describe what happens to the coins when the turntable turns at
    (a) $6\,\text{rad s}^{-1}$ **(b)** $8\,\text{rad s}^{-1}$ **(c)** $10\,\text{rad s}^{-1}$.

(ii) What would happen if the coins were interchanged?

3 A car is travelling at a steady speed of $15\,\text{ms}^{-1}$ round a roundabout of radius 20 m.

(i) Criticise this false argument:

The car is travelling at a steady speed and so its speed is neither increasing nor decreasing and therefore the car has no acceleration.

(ii) Calculate the magnitude of the acceleration of the car.

(iii) The car has mass 800 kg. Calculate the sideways force on each wheel assuming it to be the same for all four wheels.

(iv) Is the assumption in part (iii) realistic?

4 A fairground ride has seats at 3 m and at 4.5 m from the centre of rotation. Each rider travels in a horizontal circle. Say whether each of the following statements is true, giving your reasons.

(i) Riders in the two positions have the same angular speed at any time.

(ii) Riders in the two positions have the same speed at any time.

(iii) Riders in the two positions have the same magnitude of acceleration at any time.

5 A skater of mass 60 kg follows a circular path of radius 4 m, moving at $2\,ms^{-1}$.
   (i) Calculate:
      (a) the angular speed of the skater
      (b) the magnitude of the acceleration of the skater
      (c) the resultant force acting on the skater.
   (ii) What modelling assumptions have you made?

6 Two spin driers, both of which rotate about a vertical axis, have different specifications as given in the table below.

Model	Rate of rotation	Drum diameter
A	600 rpm	60 cm
B	800 rpm	40 cm

State, with reasons, which model you would expect to be the more effective.

7 A satellite of mass M_s is in a circular orbit around the earth, with a radius of r metres. The force of attraction between the earth and the satellite is given by

$$F = \frac{GM_eM_s}{r^2}$$

where $G = 6.67 \times 10^{-11}$ in S.I. units. The mass of the earth M_e is 5.97×10^{24} kg.
   (i) Find, in terms of r, expressions for
      (a) the speed of the satellite, $v\,ms^{-1}$
      (b) the time, T s, it takes to complete one revolution.
   (ii) Hence show that, for all satellites, T^2 is proportional to r^3.

A geostationary satellite orbits the earth so that it is always above the same place on the equator.
   (iii) How far is it from the centre of the earth?

(The law found in part (ii) was discovered experimentally by Johannes Kepler (1571–1630) to hold true for the planets as they orbit the sun, and is commonly known as Kepler's third law.)

8 In this question you should assume that the orbit of the earth around the sun is circular, with radius 1.44×10^{11} m, and that the sun is fixed.

(i) Find the magnitude of the acceleration of the earth as it orbits the sun.

The force of attraction between the earth and the sun is given by

$$F = \frac{GM_eM_s}{r^2}$$

where M_e is the mass of the earth, M_s is the mass of the sun, r the radius of the earth's orbit and G the universal constant of gravitation (6.67×10^{-11} S.I. units).

(ii) Calculate the mass of the sun.

(iii) Comment on the significance of the fact that you cannot calculate the mass of the earth from the radius of its orbit.

9 Sarah ties a model plane of mass 180 g to the end of a piece of string 80 cm long and then swings it round so that the plane travels in a horizontal circle. The plane is not designed to fly and there is no lift force acting on its wings.

(i) Explain why it is not possible for the string to be horizontal.

Sarah gives the plane an angular speed of 120 rpm.

(ii) What is the angular speed in radians per second?

(iii) Copy the diagram below and mark in the tension in the string, the weight of the plane and the direction of the acceleration.

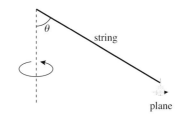

(iv) Write down the horizontal radial equation of motion for the plane and the vertical equilibrium equation in terms of the angle θ.

(v) Show that under these conditions θ has a value between 85° and 86°.

(vi) Find the tension in the string.

10 A rotary lawn mower uses a piece of light nylon string with a small metal sphere on the end to cut the grass. The string is 20 cm in length and the mass of the sphere is 30 g.

(i) Find the tension in the string when the sphere is rotating at 2000 rpm assuming the string is horizontal.

(ii) Explain why it is reasonable to assume that the string is horizontal.

(iii) Find the speed of the sphere when the tension in the string is 80 N.

11 The coefficient of friction between the tyres of a car and the road is 0.8. The mass of the car and its passengers is 800 kg. Model the car as a particle.
  (i) Find the maximum frictional force the road can exert on the car and describe what might be happening when this maximum force is acting
    (a) at right angles to the line of motion
    (b) along the line of motion.
  (ii) What is the maximum speed that the car can travel without skidding on level ground round a circular bend of radius 120 m?

The diagram shows the car, now travelling around a bend of radius 120 m on a road banked at an angle α to the horizontal. The car's speed is such that there is no sideways force (up or down the slope) exerted on its tyres by the road.

  (iii) Draw a diagram showing the weight of the car, the normal reaction of the road on it and the direction of its acceleration.
  (iv) Resolve the forces in the horizontal radial and vertical directions and write down the horizontal equation of motion and the vertical equilibrium equation.
  (v) Show that $\tan\alpha = \dfrac{v^2}{120g}$ where v is the speed of the car in metres per second.
  (vi) On this particular bend, vehicles are expected to travel at $15\,\text{ms}^{-1}$. At what angle, α, should the road be banked?

12 Experiments carried out by the police accident investigation department suggest that a typical value for a coefficient of friction between the tyres of a car and a road surface is 0.8.
  (i) Using this information, find the maximum safe speed on a level circular motorway slip road of radius 50 m.
  (ii) How much faster could cars travel if the road were banked at an angle of 5° to the horizontal?

13 An astronaut's training includes periods in a centrifuge. This may be modelled as a cage on the end of a rotating arm of length 5 m.

5 m

At a certain time, the arm is rotating at 30 rpm.

(i) Find the angular velocity of the astronaut in radians per second and her speed in metres per second.

(ii) Show that under these circumstances the astronaut is subject to an acceleration of magnitude about $5g$.

At a later stage in the training, the astronaut blacks out when her acceleration is $9g$.

(iii) Find her angular velocity (in rpm) when she blacks out.

The training is criticised on the grounds that, in flight, astronauts are not subject to rotation and the angular speed is too great. An alternative design is considered in which the astronaut is situated in a carriage driven round a circular railway track. The device must be able to simulate accelerations of up to $10g$ and the carriage can be driven at up to $100\,\mathrm{ms}^{-1}$.

(iv) What should be the radius of the circular railway track?

14 A big wheel at a fairground is rotating in a vertical circle at a constant rate of one revolution per minute.

(i) Calculate the angular speed of the wheel in radians per second.

(ii) Calculate the linear speed of a point 10 m from the axis of rotation.

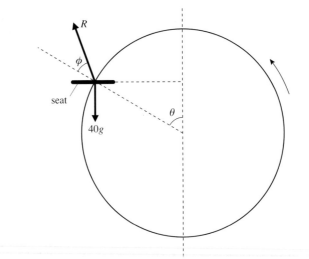

A child of mass 40 kg is sitting 10 m from the axis of rotation on a seat on the wheel. The situation may be modelled by assuming that there is negligible distance between the seat and the child's centre of mass and that the seat remains horizontal at all times. When the radius joining the seat to the axis is inclined at θ to the upward vertical, the reaction R of the seat on the child is inclined at ϕ to that radius, as shown in the diagram.

(iii) By resolving the forces acting on the child in a direction perpendicular to the radius explain why

$$R\sin\phi = 40g\sin\theta.$$

(iv) Write down the equation of motion of the child in the radial direction.

(v) Given that $\theta = \dfrac{\pi}{6}$, find R and ϕ.

[MEI]

15 A light, inelastic string of length $2a$ is attached to fixed points A and B where A is vertically above B and the distance AB $< 2a$. A small, smooth ring, P, of mass m slides on the string and is moving in a horizontal circle at a constant angular speed ω. The string sections AP and PB are straight and there is the same tension, T, in each section. The distance AP is x and AP and PB make angles α and β respectively with the vertical, as shown in the diagram.

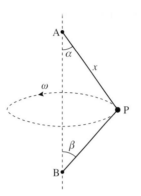

(i) Show that $x\sin\alpha = (2a - x)\sin\beta$.

(ii) By considering the vertical components of forces on the ring, explain why $x > a$.

(iii) By considering the radial motion of the ring, show that
$T(\sin\alpha + \sin\beta) = mx\omega^2\sin\alpha$.

(iv) Using your answer to part (i), show that the tension in the string is

$$\frac{mx\omega^2(2a - x)}{2a}.$$

[MEI]

16 Whilst waiting for clearance to land, aircraft are told to fly a fixed pattern in a 'holding area'. For one airport the pattern is a horizontal circuit consisting of two semi-circles connected by straight lines. The plan is shown in the diagram below.

An aircraft flies at a constant speed taking 60 s for each semi-circle.

(i) Find the angular speed about C_1 of the aircraft when flying the semi-circle centre C_1.

When flying the semi-circle the aircraft is banked at $26°$ to the horizontal. The forces acting on the banked aircraft flying in a circle about the point C_1 are shown in the diagram below. The aircraft has mass M kg and a lift force L N.

(ii) Copy this diagram and mark in the direction of the acceleration. Write down equations for the vertical and radial components of motion of the aircraft. Hence deduce the radius of the semi-circle and show that the speed of the aircraft is about 91.3 ms^{-1}.

Whilst the aircraft is flying at 1230 m above horizontal ground a wheel falls off.

(iii) Neglecting air resistance, show that the wheel travels a horizontal distance of about 1446 m before hitting the ground.

The locus of possible landing points of the wheel is shown in the diagram below.

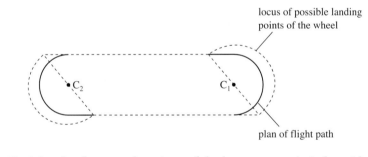

(iv) Explain why the curved sections of the locus are semi-circles with C_1 and C_2 as centres and find the common radius of these semi-circles.

[MEI]

Circular motion with variable speed

On page 7 you met the general expressions for the acceleration of a particle in circular motion:

- the *transverse component of acceleration* is $r\dot{\omega}$ or $r\ddot{\theta}$ along the tangent
- the *radial component of acceleration* is $-r\omega^2$ or $-r\dot{\theta}^2$ along the radius.

For circular motion with variable speed, the radial component, $-r\dot{\theta}^2$, is the same as that for circular motion with constant speed. The effect of the varying speed appears in the transverse component, $r\ddot{\theta}$.

On page 2, the speed was found by differentiating $s = r\theta$ with respect to time to give $\dot{s} = r\dot{\theta}$. The transverse component of acceleration for circular motion turns out to be the result of differentiating again: $\ddot{s} = r\ddot{\theta}$.

The symbols $\ddot{\theta}$ and $\dot{\omega}$ denote the rate of change of the angular velocity, or the *angular acceleration*. This quantity is measured in radians per second squared (rad s^{-2}).

In the next two sections you will be studying two types of circular motion with variable speed:

1 motion with constant angular acceleration
2 unforced motion in a vertical circle.

Circular motion with constant angular acceleration

When the angular acceleration of a body moving in a circle is constant, it is convenient to use a standard notation

$$\ddot{\theta} = \alpha.$$

You can find the angular speed and the angular displacement by integrating this with respect to time:

$$\dot{\theta} = \alpha t + c \quad \text{for some constant } c.$$

It is usual to call the initial angular speed ω_0. In this case $\dot{\theta} = \omega_0$ when $t = 0$, so $c = \omega_0$.

This gives $\quad \dot{\theta} = \omega_0 + \alpha t \quad$ or $\quad \omega = \omega_0 + \alpha t.$

Integrating again and assuming that $\theta = 0$ when $t = 0$:

$$\theta = \omega_0 t + \tfrac{1}{2}\alpha t^2.$$

These two equations may look familiar to you. They are very much like the equations for motion in a straight line with constant acceleration:

$$v = u + at$$
and $\quad s = ut + \tfrac{1}{2}at^2.$

There is a direct correspondence between the variables.

Motion in a straight line with constant acceleration	s	u	v	a
Circular motion with constant angular acceleration	θ	ω_0	$\omega \; (=\dot{\theta})$	α

In fact it can be shown that each equation for motion in a straight line with constant acceleration corresponds to an equation for circular motion with constant angular acceleration.

$$v = u + at \longleftrightarrow \omega = \omega_0 + \alpha t$$
$$s = ut + \tfrac{1}{2}at^2 \longleftrightarrow \theta = \omega_0 t + \tfrac{1}{2}\alpha t^2$$
$$v^2 = u^2 + 2as \longleftrightarrow \omega^2 = \omega_0^2 + 2\alpha\theta$$
$$s = \tfrac{1}{2}(u + v)t \longleftrightarrow \theta = \tfrac{1}{2}(\omega_0 + \omega)t$$

EXAMPLE 1.7

Oliver is standing on a playground roundabout at a distance of 2 m from the centre. Imogen pushes the roundabout with constant angular acceleration for 2 s and in this time the angular speed increases from 0.3 rad s^{-1} to 1.5 rad s^{-1}. Find

(i) the angular acceleration of the roundabout
(ii) the magnitude and direction of the resultant horizontal force acting on Oliver just before Imogen stops pushing the roundabout. (Oliver's mass is 40 kg.)

SOLUTION

(i) Using the standard notation: $\omega_0 = 0.3$, $\omega = 1.5$, $t = 2$. To find α the required equation is:

$$\omega = \omega_0 + \alpha t$$
$$\Rightarrow \quad 1.5 = 0.3 + 2\alpha$$
$$\Rightarrow \quad \alpha = 0.6$$

The angular acceleration is 0.6 rad s^{-2}

(ii)

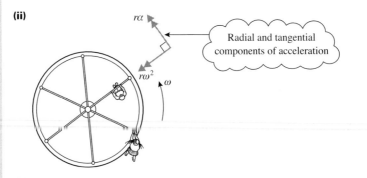

Radial and tangential components of acceleration

Figure 1.19

Just before Imogen stops pushing, Oliver's acceleration has two horizontal components.

Transverse motion
$$r\ddot{\theta} = r\alpha$$
$$= 2 \times 0.6$$
$$= 1.2 \, (\text{ms}^{-2})$$

Radial motion towards the centre:
$$r\dot{\theta}^2 = r\omega^2$$
$$= 2 \times 1.5^2$$
$$= 4.5 \, (\text{ms}^{-2})$$

The resultant acceleration has two perpendicular components $1.2 \, \text{ms}^{-2}$ and $4.5 \, \text{ms}^{-2}$. Its magnitude is $\sqrt{1.2^2 + 4.5^2}$ or $4.66 \, \text{ms}^{-2}$ and it makes an angle $\arctan\left(\frac{4.5}{1.2}\right)$ or $75°$ (to the nearest degree) with the transverse direction shown.

By Newton's second law, the resultant horizontal force is given by

$$F = ma$$
$$= 40 \times 4.66 \, \text{N}.$$

So the resultant force is $186 \, \text{N}$ (to 3 s.f.) at $75°$ to the transverse direction.

1 A flywheel is initially rotating at $6 \, \text{rad s}^{-1}$. After 5 minutes it comes to rest. Find
   (i)   the angular deceleration of the flywheel (assumed constant)
   (ii) the total angle through which it turns before coming to rest.

2 A skater spins at 1 revolution per second with her arms out sideways horizontally. She then takes 2 s to lower her arms and increases her angular speed to 3 revolutions per second. Find
   (i)   the angular acceleration in rad s^{-2} (assumed constant)
   (ii) the number of complete revolutions she makes during the 2 s while she is lowering her arms.

3 A disc slides round a horizontal circular track of radius 2 m. Its initial speed is $8 \, \text{ms}^{-1}$ and it has a constant transverse deceleration of $0.001 \, \text{ms}^{-2}$.
   (i)   Calculate the initial angular velocity of the disc.
   (ii)   Calculate the angular deceleration of the disc.
   (iii) Calculate the total angle through which the disc travels before coming to rest.
   (iv)   Calculate the distance travelled by the disc before it comes to rest.

4 In a model of a discus throw, the discus is rotated in a horizontal circle of radius 0.75 m with steadily increasing angular speed up to the moment of release. The athlete starts from rest and takes 1.5 seconds to do 1.5 revolutions before releasing the discus. With what speed is it thrown?

5 The diagram shows the Big Wheel at a fairground. It has radius 3 m. Once it is loaded with passengers it is given a uniform angular acceleration for 20 s then runs at uniform angular speed for 2 minutes. It then slows down at a uniform rate over a further 10 s. During the main part of the ride, the wheel completes 1 revolution every 10 s.

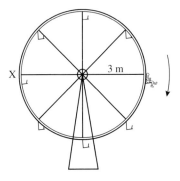

(i)   Draw a graph showing the angular speed of the wheel against time and state what information is given by the area under the graph.

(ii) Find the total angle through which a passenger moves and the distance the passenger travels.

(iii) Find the magnitude of the acceleration of a passenger at the top of the ride when it is travelling at maximum speed. Draw a force diagram to show the forces on a passenger of mass 20 kg at the highest point of the ride.

(iv) Describe the acceleration vector of a passenger who is at a point X when the wheel is half-way through its acceleration phase.

Motion in a vertical circle

Figure 1.20 shows the forces acting on a particle of mass m undergoing free circular motion in a vertical plane. For free motion it is assumed that there is no transverse force.

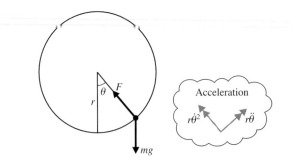

Figure 1.20

For circular motion to take place, there must be a resultant force acting on the particle towards the centre of the circle, so there must be an applied central force, F. When the circle is vertical, the force of gravity also acts in this plane, and is therefore relevant to the motion. When the particle is in the position shown in the diagram, Newton's second law gives the following equations.

Towards the centre $\qquad F - mg\cos\theta = mr\dot{\theta}^2$ ①

Transverse motion $\qquad -mg\sin\theta = mr\ddot{\theta}$ ②

The force F in the first equation might be the tension in a string or the normal reaction from a surface. This force will vary with θ and so equation ① is not helpful in describing how θ varies with time. The second equation, however, does not involve F and may be written as

$$\frac{d^2\theta}{dt^2} = -\frac{g}{r}\sin\theta$$

This differential equation can be solved, using suitable calculus techniques, to obtain an expression for θ in terms of t. The work is beyond the scope of this book but you will meet it in *Differential Equations*.

Using conservation of energy

A different (and at this stage more profitable) approach is to consider the energy of the particle. There is no motion in the radial direction, so F does no work. Gravity is the only other force acting so you can apply the principle of conservation of mechanical energy.

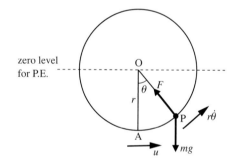

Figure 1.21

Assume that u is the speed of the particle at A, the lowest point of the circle, and that the zero level of gravitational potential energy is through the centre of the circle, O, as shown in figure 1.21.

The total energy at A is $\qquad \frac{1}{2}mu^2 - mgr$

$\qquad\qquad\qquad\qquad\quad$ (K.E.) $\quad$ (P.E.)

The total energy at P is $\qquad \frac{1}{2}m(r\dot{\theta})^2 - mgr\cos\theta$

$\qquad\qquad\qquad\qquad\quad$ (K.E.) $\qquad$ (P.E.)

By the principle of conservation of energy

$$\tfrac{1}{2}m(r\dot\theta)^2 - mgr\cos\theta = \tfrac{1}{2}mu^2 - mgr$$

$$\Rightarrow \quad r\dot\theta^2 = \frac{u^2}{r} - 2g(1 - \cos\theta)$$

This tells you the angular speed, $\dot\theta$, of the particle when OP is at any angle θ to OA.

The next two examples show how conservation of energy may be applied to theoretical models of problems involving motion in a vertical circle.

EXAMPLE 1.8

A particle of mass 0.03 kg is attached to the end, P, of a light rod OP of length 0.5 m which is free to rotate in a vertical circle with centre O. The particle is set in motion starting at the lowest point of the circle.

The initial speed of the particle is $2\,\text{ms}^{-1}$.

(i) Find the initial kinetic energy of the particle.
(ii) Find an expression for the potential energy gained when the rod has turned through an angle θ.
(iii) Find the value of θ when the particle first comes to rest.
(iv) Find the stress in the rod at this point, stating whether it is a tension or a thrust.
(v) Repeat parts (i) to (iv) using an initial speed of $4\,\text{ms}^{-1}$.
(vi) Why is it possible for the first motion (when $v_0 = 2$) to take place if the rod is replaced by a string, but not the second (when $v_0 = 4$)?

SOLUTION

(i) $$\text{Kinetic energy} = \tfrac{1}{2}mv^2$$
$$= \tfrac{1}{2} \times 0.03 \times 2^2$$
$$= 0.06$$

The initial kinetic energy is 0.06 J.

(ii) Figure 1.22 shows the position of the particle when the rod has rotated through an angle θ.

Figure 1.22

It has risen a distance AN where

$$AN = OA - ON$$
$$= 0.5 - 0.5\cos\theta$$
$$= 0.5(1 - \cos\theta)$$

The gain in potential energy at P is therefore

$$0.03g \times 0.5(1 - \cos\theta) = 0.015g(1 - \cos\theta)\,\text{J}$$

(iii) When the particle first comes to rest, the kinetic energy is zero, so by the principle of conservation of energy:

$$0.015g(1 - \cos\theta) = 0.06$$
$$1 - \cos\theta = \frac{0.06}{0.015g}$$
$$= 0.408\ldots$$
$$\Rightarrow \quad \cos\theta = 0.592$$
$$\theta = 0.938\,\text{rad, i.e. about } 53.7°$$

(iv) The forces acting on the particle and its acceleration are as shown in figure 1.23.

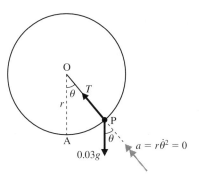

Figure 1.23

The component of the acceleration towards the centre of the circle is $r\dot\theta^2$ which equals zero when the angular speed is zero. Resolving towards the centre:

$$T - 0.03g\cos\theta = 0 \qquad\qquad ①$$
$$T = 0.174$$

Since this is positive the stress in the rod is a tension. Its magnitude is 0.174 N.

(v) When the initial speed is $4\,\text{ms}^{-1}$, the initial kinetic energy is

$$\tfrac{1}{2} \times 0.03 \times 4^2 = 0.24\,\text{J.}$$

The gain in potential energy at P, as shown in part (ii), is

$$0.015g(1 - \cos\theta)\,\text{J.}$$

When the particle first comes to rest, the kinetic energy is zero, so by the principle of conservation of energy:

$$0.015g(1 - \cos\theta) = 0.24$$
$$\cos\theta = -0.6327$$
$$\theta = 2.256 \text{ rad, i.e. about } 129°.$$

Now equation ① gives the tension in the rod as

$$T = 0.03g\cos\theta = -0.186$$

The negative tension means that the stress is in fact a thrust of 0.186 N. Figure 1.24 illustrates the forces acting in this position.

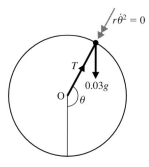

Figure 1.24

(vi) A string cannot exert a thrust so, although the rod could be replaced by a string in the first case, it would be impossible in the second. In the absence of any radial thrust the particle will leave its circular path at the point where the tension is zero and before reaching the position where the velocity is zero.

EXAMPLE 1.9

A bead of mass 0.01 kg is threaded on a smooth circular wire of radius 0.6 m and is set in motion with a speed of u ms^{-1} at the bottom of the circle. This just enables the bead to reach the top of the wire.

(i) Find the value of u.

(ii) What is the direction of the reaction of the wire on the bead when the bead is at the top of the circle?

SOLUTION

(i) The initial kinetic energy is

$$\tfrac{1}{2} \times 0.01u^2 = 0.005u^2$$

The bead will just reach the top if the speed there is zero. If this is the case, its kinetic energy at the top will also be zero.

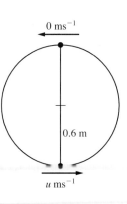

Figure 1.25

It has then risen a height of 2×0.6 m or 1.2 m, so its gain in potential energy is

$$0.01g \times 1.2 = 0.012g$$

By the principle of conservation of energy,

$$\text{loss in K.E.} = \text{gain in P.E.}$$
$$0.005u^2 = 0.012g$$
$$u^2 = 2.4g$$
$$u = \sqrt{2.4g}$$

The initial speed must be 4.85 ms^{-1} (to 2 d.p.).

(ii) The reaction of the wire on the bead could be directed either towards the centre of the circle or away from it. The bead has zero angular speed at the top so the component of its acceleration, and therefore the resultant force towards the centre, is zero. The reaction must be outwards, as shown in figure 1.26, and equal to $0.01g$ N.

Figure 1.26

 Would this motion be possible if the bead were tied to the end of a string instead of being threaded on a wire?

The breakdown of circular motion

⚠ When carrying out this activity, keep well away from other people and breakable objects.

Tie a small object on the end of a piece of strong thread and tie the other end loosely (to minimise friction) round a smooth knitting needle (or a smooth rod with a cork on one end).

Hold the pointed end of the needle and make the object move in a vertical circle as shown in figure 1.27.

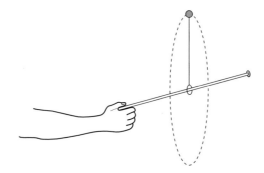

Figure 1.27

Demonstrate these three types of motion.

1 The object travels in complete circles.
2 The object swings like a pendulum.
3 The object rises above the level of the needle but then fails to complete a full circle.

What would happen if the string broke?
What would happen if a rod were used rather than a string?

The three different types of motion mentioned in the activity and the case in which the string breaks are illustrated in the diagrams.

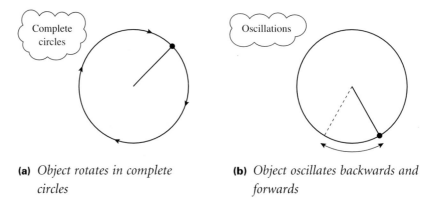

(a) *Object rotates in complete circles*

(b) *Object oscillates backwards and forwards*

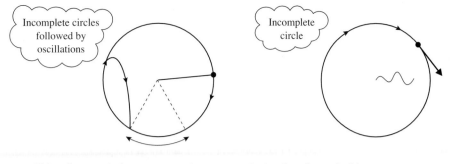

(c) *Object leaves circle at some point and falls inwards*

(d) *String breaks and object starts to move away along a tangent*

Figure 1.28

Modelling the breakdown of circular motion

For what reasons might something depart from motion in a circle? For example, under what conditions will a particle attached to a string and moving in a vertical circle fall out of the circle? Under what conditions will a bicycle travelling over a speed bump with circular cross-section leave the road?

A particle on a string

Figure 1.29 shows a particle P of mass m attached to a string of length r, rotating with angular speed ω in a vertical circle, centre O.

Figure 1.29

There are two forces acting on the particle, its weight, mg, and the tension, T, in the string. The acceleration of the particle is $r\omega^2$ towards the centre of the circle.

Applying Newton's second law towards the centre gives

$$T + mg\cos\alpha = mr\omega^2 \qquad \text{①}$$

where α is the angle shown in the diagram.

While the particle is in circular motion the string is taut, and so $T > 0$. The instant it starts to leave the circle the string goes slack and $T = 0$.

Substituting $T = 0$ in ① gives

$$mg\cos\alpha = mr\omega^2$$

$$\Rightarrow \quad \cos\alpha = \frac{r\omega^2}{g}$$

The equation

$$\cos\alpha = \frac{r\omega^2}{g}$$

allows you to find the angle α at which the particle leaves the circle, if it does. The greatest possible value for $\cos\alpha$ is 1, so if $\dfrac{r\omega^2}{g}$ is greater than 1 throughout the motion, the equation has no solution and this means that the particle never leaves the circle. Thus the condition for the particle to stay in circular motion is that $\omega^2 \geqslant \dfrac{g}{r}$ throughout.

In this example, of a particle on the end of a string, ω varies throughout the motion. As you saw on page 32, the value of ω at any instant is given by the energy equation, which in this case is

$$\tfrac{1}{2}mr^2\omega^2 + mgr(1 + \cos\alpha) = \tfrac{1}{2}mu^2$$

where u is the speed of the particle at the lowest point.

A particle moving on the inside of a vertical circle

The same analysis applies to a particle sliding around the inside of a smooth circle. The only difference is that in this case the tension, T, is replaced by the normal reaction, R, of the surface on the particle (see figure 1.30). When $R = 0$ the particle leaves the surface.

Figure 1.30

? In the toy shown in the photograph on page 38, the track exerts a downwards force on the car as it moves around the top of the circle. What would you feel if you *gently* touched the top of the track at this instant?

A particle moving on the outside of a vertical circle

The forces acting on a particle moving on the outside of a vertical circle, such as a car going over a hump-backed bridge are the normal reaction, R, acting outwards and the weight of the particle, as shown in figure 1.31.

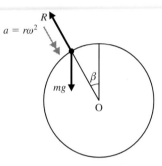

Figure 1.31

Applying Newton's second law towards the centre gives

$$mg\cos\beta - R = mr\omega^2 \qquad \text{②}$$

where β is the angle shown.

If the normal reaction is zero it means there is no force between the particle and the surface and so the particle is leaving the surface.

Substituting $R = 0$ in ② gives

$$mg\cos\beta = mr\omega^2$$
$$\Rightarrow \quad \cos\beta = \frac{r\omega^2}{g}$$

? The conditions for the breakdown of circular motion seem to be the same in the cases of a particle on the end of a string and a particle on the outside of a circle. However, everyday experience tells you that circular motion on the end of a string is only possible if the angular speed is large enough whereas a particle will only stay on the outside of a circle if the angular speed is small enough.

How do the conditions $T > 0$ and $R > 0$ explain this difference?

EXAMPLE 1.10

Determine whether it is possible for a particle, P, of mass m kg to be in the position shown in figure 1.32, moving round a vertical circle of radius 0.5 m with an instant angular speed of 4 rad s^{-1} when it is

(i) sliding on the outside of a smooth surface

(ii) sliding on the inside of a smooth surface

(iii) attached to the end of a string OP

(iv) threaded on a smooth vertical ring.

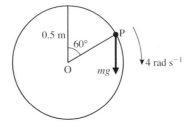

Figure 1.32

SOLUTION

(i) On the outside of a smooth surface:

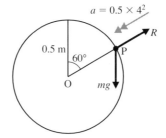

Figure 1.33

The normal reaction R N of the surface on the particle must be acting outwards, so Newton's second law towards the centre gives

$$mg\cos60° - R = m \times 0.5 \times 4^2$$

$$\Rightarrow \quad R = mg\cos60° - 8m$$

$$= -3.1m$$

Whatever the mass, m, this negative value of R is impossible, so the motion is impossible. The particle will already have left the surface.

(ii) On the inside of a smooth surface:

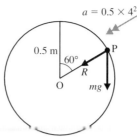

Figure 1.34

The normal reaction of the surface on the particle will now be acting towards the centre and so

$$R + mg\cos 60° = m \times 0.5 \times 4^2$$

$$\Rightarrow \quad R = +3.1m$$

This is possible.

(iii) Attached to the end of a string:
This example is like part (ii) since the tension acts towards the centre, so the motion is possible.

(iv) Threaded on a smooth ring:
If the particle is threaded on a ring the normal reaction can act inwards or outwards so the motion can take place whatever the angular speed. This is also the case when a particle is attached to the centre by a light rod. The rod will exert a tension or a thrust as required.

 Which of the situations in the previous example are possible when the instant angular speed is $3\,\text{rad}\,\text{s}^{-1}$?

EXAMPLE 1.11 Eddie, a skier of mass m kg, is skiing down a hillside when he reaches a smooth hump in the form of an arc AB of a circle centre O and radius 8 m as shown in figure 1.35. O, A and B lie in a vertical plane and OA and OB make angles of $20°$ and $40°$ with the vertical respectively. Eddie's speed at A is $7\,\text{ms}^{-1}$. Determine whether Eddie will lose contact with the ground before reaching the point B.

Figure 1.35

SOLUTION

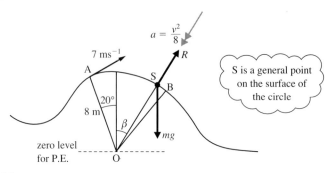

Figure 1.36

Taking the zero level for potential energy to be a horizontal line through O, the initial energy at A is

$$\tfrac{1}{2} m \times 7^2 + mg \times 8\cos20°$$

The energy at any point S is

$$\tfrac{1}{2} mv^2 + mg \times 8\cos\beta$$

By the principle of conservation of energy these are equal.

$$\tfrac{1}{2} mv^2 + mg \times 8\cos\beta = \tfrac{1}{2} m \times 7^2 + mg \times 8\cos20°$$
$$\Rightarrow \quad v^2 + 16g\cos\beta = 49 + 147.34$$
$$\Rightarrow \quad v^2 = 196.34 - 16g\cos\beta \qquad \text{①}$$

Using Newton's second law towards the centre of the circle

$$mg\cos\beta - R = m\frac{v^2}{8}$$
$$\Rightarrow \quad R = m\left(g\cos\beta - \frac{v^2}{8}\right)$$

If Eddie leaves the circle at point S, then $R = 0$

$$\Rightarrow \quad v^2 = 8g\cos\beta$$

Substituting in ①

$$8g\cos\beta = 196.34 - 16g\cos\beta$$
$$\Rightarrow \quad 24g\cos\beta = 196.34$$

This gives $\beta \approx 33.4°$, which is less than $40°$, so Eddie will lose contact with the ground before he reaches the point B.

1 The diagrams show two particles of mass m kg moving in vertical circles. Their angular speeds and positions are as shown.

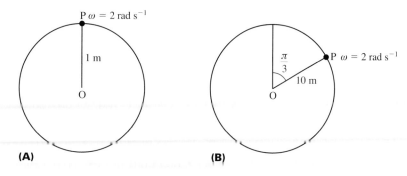

(A)　　　　　　　　　　　　　　(B)

(i) Write down the components of their accelerations along PO.

(ii) By considering the forces acting on the particle, determine in each case whether it is possible for it to be moving with this speed in this position when it is:

(a) sliding on the outside of a smooth surface

(b) sliding on the inside of a smooth surface

(c) attached to the end of a string OP

(d) threaded on a smooth ring in a vertical plane.

2 Each of the following diagrams shows a bead of mass m which is sliding in a vertical plane on a smooth circular wire. Initially it is in the position shown and moving with the given speed.

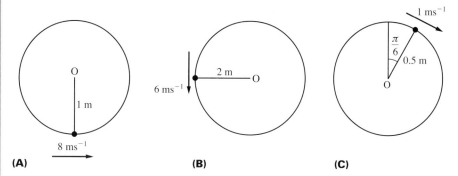

(A)　　　　　　　　　　　　(B)　　　　　　　　　(C)

In each case:

(i) Using the horizontal through the centre of the circle as the zero level for potential energy, write down the total initial mechanical energy of the bead.

(ii) Decide whether the bead will make complete revolutions or whether it will come to rest below the highest point. If it makes complete revolutions, determine the speed at the top. Otherwise find the height above the centre when it comes to rest.

(iii) Assuming that the bead is moving under the action of its weight and a radial force only, find the magnitude and direction of the radial force

(a) initially

(b) when it reaches the top or comes to rest.

3 The diagram shows a model car track. You may assume that all parts of the track lie in the same vertical plane.

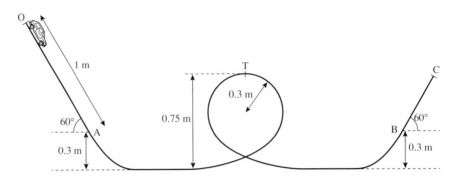

Between A and B the track is symmetrical about a vertical line through T and its length from A to T is 2.1 m. OA and BC are straight and the top of the loop is an arc of radius 0.3 m. For a car of mass m kg, there is a frictional resistance of $0.06mg$ N.

The car starts from rest at the point O.

(i) Find the work done against friction between O and T.

(ii) Use the work–energy principle to show that the kinetic energy at T is $0.230mg$ J.

(iii) By considering circular motion at T, show that the car will move right round the loop in contact with the track.

(iv) The car stops at C before returning. Find the length BC.

(v) Will the car reach T on the return journey?

4 A metal sphere of mass 0.5 kg is moving in a vertical circle of radius 0.8 m at the end of a light, inelastic string. At the top of the circle the sphere has speed $3\,\text{ms}^{-1}$.

(i) Calculate the gravitational potential energy lost by the sphere when it reaches the bottom of the circle and hence calculate its speed at this point.

(ii) Find an expression for the speed of the sphere when the string makes an angle, θ, with the upward vertical.

(iii) Find the tension in the string when the sphere is

   (a) at the top

   (b) at the bottom point of the circle.

(iv) Draw a diagram showing the forces acting on the sphere when the string makes an angle θ with the upward vertical. Find expressions for the tension in the string and the transverse component of the sphere's acceleration at this instant.

5 A glider is travelling horizontally until the pilot executes a loop-the-loop manoeuvre as shown in the diagram. The loop may be modelled as a vertical circle. The glider is initially at a height of 700 m, travelling at 30 ms⁻¹. The bottom of the loop is at height 400 m and the radius of the loop is 100 m.

Assuming that the mechanical energy is conserved, calculate:
(i) the speed of the glider at the lowest and highest points of the loop
(ii) the magnitude of the acceleration of the glider at the lowest and highest points of the loop.

The mass of the pilot is 70 kg.
(iii) Draw diagrams to show the reaction forces acting on him at the lowest and highest points of the loop and state their magnitudes.
(iv) What would happen if he attempted a loop of radius 150 m, starting from the same lowest point?
(v) What is the maximum radius for a successful loop from this point?

6 As a challenge, a girl is required to swing a bucket of water in a vertical circular arc above her head. If the bucket is not moving fast enough she will get wet. This may be modelled by taking the girl's arm to be 55 cm long and the bucket 35 cm from base to handle. The handle is taken to be rigidly attached to the bucket and is held firmly so that her arm is always in line with the centre of the base. Assume the water behaves as a solid block.

The girl considers three possible depths of water in the bucket: 5 cm, 10 cm and 15 cm.
(i) For which depth does she need to give the bucket the highest angular speed?

In the event she is forced to have 15 cm of water in the bucket.
(ii) Find the minimum angular speed at the top of the arc for the water to stay in the bucket.
(iii) Deduce the *average* angular acceleration the girl must give the bucket, assuming it is at rest at the lowest point.

One girl, doing this for real, ended with the bucket as well as the water hitting her head.
(iv) What might have happened?

7 The diagram shows a ride at an amusement park. The loop is, to good approximation, a circle of radius 8 m, in a vertical plane.

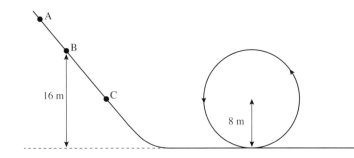

In answering the following questions, you should assume that no energy is lost to forces such as friction and air resistance and the car starts from rest.

(i) Explain why a car which starts just above point B, 16 m above ground level, will not complete the loop.

(ii) For a car to complete the loop successfully it must start at or above point A. What is the height of A?

(iii) On 'Kiddie days' the organisers start the car below point C. Describe what happens to the car and state the maximum height of point C for it to be safe.

8 The diagram illustrates an old road bridge over a river. The road surface follows an approximately circular arc with radius 15 m.

A car is being driven across the bridge and you should model it as a particle.

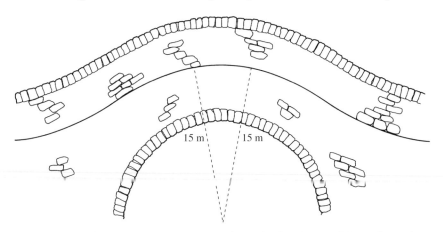

(i) Calculate the greatest constant speed at which it is possible to drive the car across the bridge without it leaving the road, giving your answer both in ms^{-1} and in mph.

(ii) Comment on the fact that the bridge is old.

(iii) How is it possible to improve the design of the bridge?

9 A car of mass 200 kg travels along the track of a roller-coaster. In one section of the track, the car travels around the inside of a vertical circle of radius 10 m as shown in the diagram.

The car is attached to the track so that it can move freely along it, but cannot leave the circular path. While the car is travelling around the circle, there is no driving force present. Friction and air resistance may be neglected.

The car enters the circle at its lowest point, A, with a speed of 21 ms^{-1}.

(i) Show that the speed of the car at the highest point is 7 ms^{-1}.

(ii) Find the radial acceleration at the highest point. Hence calculate the force that the track exerts on the car at this point. Could the roller-coaster operate if the car was not attached to the track?
Explain your answer briefly.

(iii) Calculate the radial and tangential components of acceleration when the car has travelled through 120° round the circle from A. Show that the resultant acceleration at this point is directed towards A.

[MEI]

10 A particle of mass m is attached to one end, A, of a light, inelastic string of length l. The other end, B, of the string is attached to a ceiling so that the particle is free to swing in a vertical plane; the angle between the string and the downward vertical is θ rad. You may assume that the air resistance on the particle is negligible.

Initially $\theta = \dfrac{\pi}{3}$ and the particle is released from rest.

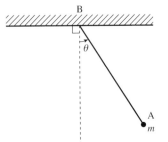

(i) Show that the potential energy lost by the particle since leaving its initial position is $\dfrac{mgl}{2}(2\cos\theta - 1)$. Hence find an expression for v^2, where v is the linear speed of the particle, in terms of l, g and θ.

(ii) Show that the tension in the string at any point of the motion is $mg(3\cos\theta - 1)$.

(iii) Find the greatest tension in the string. What is the position of the particle when the tension in the string is greatest?

Before its release with $\theta = \dfrac{\pi}{3}$, the particle is held in position by means of a second light string inclined at an acute angle, α, to the downward vertical, as shown in the diagram below. The second string is cut to allow the particle to swing.

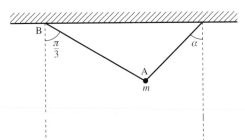

(iv) What is the direction of the acceleration of the particle just after the string is cut?

You are given that the tension in the string AB when the particle is being supported is

$$\frac{2mg}{1 + \sqrt{3}\cot\alpha}.$$

(v) Calculate the value of α for which the tension in AB remains unchanged when the string is cut.

[MEI]

Hammer throwing

Investigate the action of throwing the hammer. Estimate the maximum tension in the wire for a top class athlete. (Data: the hammer is a ball of mass 3 kg attached to a light wire of length 1.8 m. A throw of 80 m is world class.)

Figure 1.37

Mountain biking

Why do those taking part in mountain bike rallies go home with mud on their backs?

1 Position, velocity and acceleration of a particle moving on a circle of radius r.

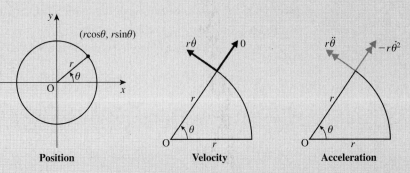

Position	Velocity	Acceleration

- position $(r\cos\theta, r\sin\theta)$
- velocity   transverse component: $v = r\dot{\theta} = r\omega$
                   radial component: 0

where $\dot{\theta}$ or ω is the angular velocity of the particle.

- acceleration   transverse component: $r\ddot{\theta} = r\dot{\omega}$

                     radial component: $-r\dot{\theta}^2 = -r\omega^2 = -\dfrac{v^2}{r}$

where $\ddot{\theta}$ or $\dot{\omega}$ is the angular acceleration of the particle.

2 By Newton's second law the forces acting on a particle of mass m in circular motion are equal to

- transverse component: $mr\dot{\omega} = mr\ddot{\theta}$

- radial component: $-\dfrac{mv^2}{r} = -mr\omega^2$

- or radial component: $+\dfrac{mv^2}{r} = +mr\omega^2$ towards the centre.

3 Problems involving free motion in a vertical circle can be solved using the principle of conservation of energy

$$\text{P.E.} + \text{K.E.} = \text{constant}$$

in conjunction with Newton's second law in the radial direction.

4 Circular motion breaks down when the available force towards the centre is $< mr\omega^2$ or $\dfrac{mv^2}{r}$.

5 The equations for circular motion with constant angular acceleration α are

- $\omega = \omega_0 + \alpha t$
- $\omega^2 = \omega_0^2 + 2\alpha\theta$
- $\theta = \omega_0 t + \frac{1}{2}\alpha t^2$
- $\theta = \frac{1}{2}(\omega_0 + \omega)t$

where ω_0 is the initial angular speed.

2 Elastic strings and springs

The only way of finding the limits of the possible is by going beyond them into the impossible.

Arthur C. Clarke

The pictures show people taking part in the sport of bunjee jumping.

This is a dangerous sport which originated in the South Sea islands where creepers were used rather than ropes. In the more modern version, a person jumps off a high bridge or crane to which he is attached by an elastic rope round his ankles.

? If somebody bunjee jumping from a bridge wants the excitement of just reaching the surface of the water below, how would you calculate the length of rope required?

The answer to this question clearly depends on the height of the bridge, the mass of the person jumping and the elasticity of the rope. All ropes are elastic to some extent, but it would be extremely dangerous to use an ordinary rope for this sport because the impulse necessary to stop somebody falling would involve a very large tension acting in the rope for a short time and this would provide too great a shock to the system. A bungee is a strong elastic rope, similar to those used to secure loads on cycles, cars or lorries, with the essential property for this sport that it allows the impulse to act over a much longer time so that the rope exerts a smaller force on the jumper.

Generally in mechanics, the word *string* is used to represent such things as ropes which can be in tension but not in compression. In this chapter you will be studying some of the properties of elastic strings and springs and will return to the problem of the bunjee jumper as a final investigation.

Strings and springs

So far in situations involving strings it has been assumed that they do not stretch when they are under tension. Such strings are called *inextensible.* For some materials this is a good assumption, but for others the length of the string increases significantly under tension. Strings and springs which stretch are said to be *elastic. Open coiled springs* are springs which can also be compressed. In this book springs are assumed to be open coiled.

The length of a string or spring when there is no force applied to it is called its *natural length.* If it is stretched, the increase in length is called its *extension* and if a spring is compressed it is said to have a *negative extension* or *compression.*

When stretched, a spring exerts an inward force, or *tension,* on whatever is attached to its ends (figure 2.1(b)). When compressed it exerts an outward force, or *thrust,* on its ends (figure 2.1(c)). An elastic string exerts a tension when stretched, but when slack exerts no force.

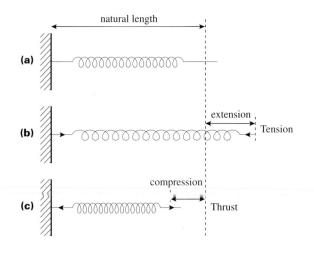

Figure 2.1

You will need some elastic strings, some open coiled springs, some weights and a support stand. Set up the apparatus as shown.

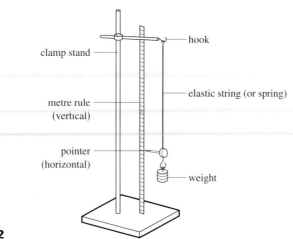

Figure 2.2

Before doing any experiments, predict the answers to the following questions:

1 How are the extension of the string and the weight hanging on it related?

2 If a string of the same material but twice the natural length has the same weight attached, how does the extension change?

3 Does the string return to its original length when unloaded
   (i) if the weight of the object is small?
   (ii) if the weight of the object is large?

Now use the apparatus to plot a graph, for each string, of tension, i.e. the weight of the object (vertical axis) against the extension (horizontal axis) to help you to answer these questions.

Design and carry out an experiment which will investigate the relationship between the thrust in an open coiled spring and the decrease in its length.

From your experiments you should have made the following observations.

● Each string or spring returned to its original length once the object was removed, up to a certain limit.

● The graph of tension or thrust against extension for each string or spring was a straight line for all or part of the data. Strings or springs which exhibit this linear behaviour are said to be *perfectly elastic*.

● The gradient of the linear part of the graph was roughly halved when the string was doubled in length.

● If you kept increasing the weight, the string or spring might have stopped stretching or might have stretched without returning to its original length. In this case the graph would no longer be a straight line: the material had passed its *elastic limit*.

- During your experiment using an open coiled spring you might have found it necessary to prevent the spring from buckling. You might also have found that there came a point when the coils were completely closed and a further decrease in length was impossible.

Hooke's law

In 1678 Robert Hooke formulated a *Rule or law of nature in every springing body* which, for small extensions relative to the length of the string or spring, can be stated as follows:

The tension in an elastic spring or string is proportional to the extension. If a spring is compressed the thrust is proportional to the decrease in length of the spring.

When a string or spring is described as elastic, it means that it is reasonable to apply the modelling assumption that it obeys Hooke's law. A further assumption, that it is light (i.e. has zero mass), is usual and is made in this book.

There are three ways in which Hooke's law is commonly expressed for a string. Which one you use depends on the extent to which you are interested in the string itself rather than just its overall properties. Denoting the natural length of the string by l_0 and its area of cross-section by A, the different forms are as follows.

- $T = \dfrac{EA}{l_0} x$ In this form E is called *Young's modulus* and is a property of the material out of which the string is formed. This form is commonly used in physics and engineering, subjects in which properties of materials are studied. It is rarely used in mathematics. The S.I. unit for Young's modulus is Nm^{-2}.

- $T = \dfrac{\lambda}{l_0} x$ The constant λ is called the *modulus of elasticity* of the string and will be the same for any string of a given cross-section made out of the same material. Many situations require knowledge of the natural length of a string and this form may well be the most appropriate in such cases. The S.I. unit for the modulus of elasticity is N.

- $T = kx$ In this simplest form, k is called the *stiffness* of the string. It is a property of the string as a whole. You may choose to use this form if neither the natural length nor the cross-sectional area of the string is relevant to the situation. The S.I. unit for stiffness is Nm^{-1}.

Notice that $k = \dfrac{\lambda}{l_0} = \dfrac{EA}{l_0}$

In this book only the forms using the modulus of elasticity and stiffness are used, and these can be applied to springs as well as strings.

EXAMPLE 2.1 A light elastic string of natural length 0.7 m and modulus of elasticity 50 N has one end fixed and a particle of mass 1.4 kg attached to the other. The system hangs vertically in equilibrium. Find the extension of the string.

SOLUTION

The forces acting on the particle are the tension, T N, upwards and the weight, $1.4g$ N, downwards.

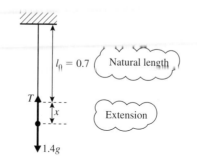

Figure 2.3

Since the particle is in equilibrium

$$T = 1.4g$$

Using Hooke's law: $T = \dfrac{\lambda}{l_0}x$

$$\Rightarrow \quad 1.4g = \dfrac{50}{0.7}x$$

$$\Rightarrow \quad x = \dfrac{0.7 \times 1.4g}{50}$$

$$= 0.192$$

The extension in the string is 0.19 m (correct to 2 s.f.).

EXAMPLE 2.2 The mechanism of a set of kitchen scales consists of a light scale pan supported on a spring. When measuring 1.5 kg of flour, the spring is compressed by 7 mm. Find

(i) the stiffness of the spring
(ii) the mass of the heaviest object that can measured if it is impossible to compress the spring by more than 15 mm.

SOLUTION

(i) The forces on the scale pan with its load of flour are the weight, $1.5g$ N, downwards, and the thrust of the spring, T N, upwards.

Figure 2.4

Since it is in equilibrium

$$T = 1.5g$$

Applying Hooke's law with stiffness $k\,\mathrm{Nm}^{-1}$

$$T = k \times 0.007$$
$$\Rightarrow \quad 1.5g = 0.007k$$
$$\Rightarrow \quad k = 2100$$

The stiffness of the spring is $2100\,\mathrm{Nm}^{-1}$.

(ii) Let the mass of the heaviest object be M kg, so the maximum thrust is Mg N. Then Hooke's law for a compression of 15 mm gives:

$$Mg = 2100 \times 0.015$$
$$\Rightarrow \quad M = 3.214\ldots$$

The mass of the heaviest object that can be measured is 3.21 kg (to 3 s.f.).

Note

These scales would probably be calibrated to a maximum of 3 kg.

EXERCISE 2A

1 A light elastic spring of stiffness k is attached to a ceiling. A block of mass m hangs in equilibrium, attached to the other end of the spring.
   (i)   Draw a diagram showing the forces acting on the block.

   The mass of the block is 0.25 kg and the extension of the spring is 0.4 m.
   (ii) Find the value of k in S.I. units.

   The natural length of the spring is 2 m.
   (iii) Find the modulus of elasticity of the spring.

2 (i)   An elastic string has natural length 20 cm. The string is fixed at one end. When a force of 20 N is applied to the other end the string doubles in length. Find the modulus of elasticity.
   (ii) Another elastic string also has natural length 20 cm. When a force of 20 N is applied to each end the string doubles in length. Find the modulus of elasticity.
   (iii) Explain the connection between the answers to parts (i) and (ii).

3 A light spring has stiffness $0.75\,\text{Nm}^{-1}$. One end is attached to a ceiling, the other to a particle of weight 0.03 N which hangs in equilibrium below the ceiling. In this situation the length of the spring is 49 cm.

(i) Find the tension in the spring.

(ii) Find the extension of the spring.

(iii) Find the natural length of the spring.

The particle is removed and replaced with one of weight w N. When this hangs in equilibrium the spring has length 60 cm.

(iv) What is the value of w?

4 An object of mass 0.5 kg is attached to an elastic string and causes an extension of 0 cm when the system hangs vertically in equilibrium.

(i) What is the tension in the string?

(ii) What is the stiffness of the string?

(iii) What is the mass of an object which causes an extension of 10 cm?

The modulus of elasticity of the string is 73.5 N.

(iv) What is the natural length of the string?

5 In this question take the value of g to be $10\,\text{ms}^{-2}$. The diagram shows a spring of natural length 60 cm which is being compressed under the weight of a block of mass m kg. Smooth supports constrain the block to move only in the vertical direction.

The modulus of elasticity of the spring is 180 N. The system is in equilibrium and the length of the spring is 50 cm. Find

(i) the thrust in the spring

(ii) the value of m

(iii) the stiffness of the spring.

More blocks are piled on.

(iv) Describe the situation when there are seven blocks in total, all identical to the first one.

6 A small sphere, A, of mass m kg moves in a circle with centre B on a smooth horizontal table. A is joined to a smoothly rotating vertical axle at B by an elastic string of natural length a m and stiffness $k\,\text{Nm}^{-1}$ and has constant angular speed $\omega\,\text{rad s}^{-1}$. Find an expression for the radius of the circle in terms of m, a, k and ω.

Using Hooke's law with more than one spring or string

Hooke's law allows you to investigate situations involving two or more springs or strings in various configurations.

EXAMPLE 2.3

A particle of mass 0.4 kg is attached to the mid-point of a light elastic string of natural length 1 m and modulus of elasticity λ N. The string is then stretched between a point A at the top of a doorway and a point B which is on the floor 2 m vertically below A.

(i) Find, in terms of λ, the extensions of the two parts of the string.

(ii) Calculate their values in the case where $\lambda = 9.8$.

(iii) Find the minimum value of λ which will ensure that the lower half of the string is not slack.

SOLUTION

For a question like this it is helpful to draw two diagrams, one showing the relevant natural lengths and extensions, and the other showing the forces acting on the particle.

Since the force of gravity acts downwards on the particle, its equilibrium position will be below the mid-point of AB. This is also shown in the diagram.

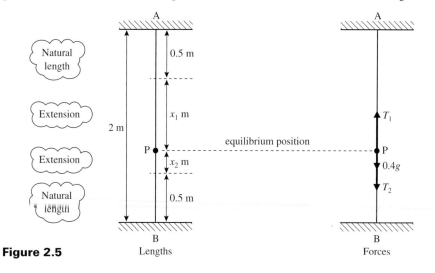

Figure 2.5   Lengths   Forces

(i) The particle is in equilibrium, so the resultant vertical force acting on it is zero.

Therefore $T_1 = T_2 + 0.4g$ ①

Hooke's law can be applied to each part of the string.

For AP: $T_1 = \dfrac{\lambda}{0.5} x_1$ ②

For BP: $$T_2 = \frac{\lambda}{0.5} x_2 \qquad \text{\scriptsize③}$$

Substituting these expressions in equation ① gives:

$$\frac{\lambda}{0.5} x_1 = \frac{\lambda}{0.5} x_2 + 0.4g$$

$$\Rightarrow \quad \lambda x_1 - \lambda x_2 = 0.5 \times 0.4g$$

$$\Rightarrow \quad x_1 - x_2 = 0.2 \frac{g}{\lambda} \qquad \text{\scriptsize④}$$

Alternatively, you can use x for x_1 and $(1-x)$ for x_2.

But from the first diagram it can be seen that

$$x_1 + x_2 = 1 \qquad \text{\scriptsize⑤}$$

Adding ④ and ⑤ gives:

$$2x_1 = 1 + 0.2 \frac{g}{\lambda} \quad \Rightarrow \quad x_1 = 0.5 + 0.1 \frac{g}{\lambda}$$

Similarly, subtracting ④ from ⑤ gives:

$$x_2 = 0.5 - 0.1 \frac{g}{\lambda} \qquad \text{\scriptsize⑥}$$

(ii) Since $\lambda = 9.8$ the extensions are 0.6 m and 0.4 m.

(iii) The lower part of the string will not become slack providing $x_2 > 0$. It follows from equation ⑥ that:

$$0.5 - 0.1 \frac{g}{\lambda} > 0$$

$$\Rightarrow \quad 0.5 > 0.1 \frac{g}{\lambda} \quad \Rightarrow \quad \lambda > 0.2g$$

The minimum value of λ for which the lower part of the string is not slack is 1.96 N, and in this case BP has zero tension.

Historical note

If you search for Robert Hooke (1635–1703) on the internet, you will find that he was a man of many parts. He was one of a talented group of polymaths (which included his rival Newton) who have had an enormous impact on scientific thought and practice. Among other things, he designed and built Robert Boyle's air pump, discovered the red spot on Jupiter and invented the balanced spring mechanism for watches. His work on microscopy led to his becoming the father of microbiology and he was the first to use the term 'cell' with respect to living things. Hooke worked closely with his friend Sir Christopher Wren in the rebuilding of the City of London after the great fire, and was responsible for the realisation of many of his designs including the Royal Greenwich Observatory. Both Hooke and Wren were astronomers and architects and they designed the Monument to the fire with a trapdoor at the top and a laboratory in the basement so that it could be used as an enormous 62 m telescope. Hooke, the great practical man, also used the column for experiments on air pressure and pendulums.

1 The diagram shows a uniform plank of weight 120 N symmetrically suspended in equilibrium by two identical elastic strings, each of natural length 0.8 m and modulus of elasticity 1200 N.

Find
  (i) the tension in each string
  (ii) the extension of each string.

The two strings are replaced by a single string, also of natural length 0.8 m, attached to the middle of the plank. The plank is in the same position.
  (iii) Find the modulus of elasticity of this string and comment on its relationship to that of the original strings.

2 The manufacturer of a sports car specifies the coil spring for the front suspension as a spring of 10 coils with a natural length 0.3 m and a compression 0.1 m when under a load of 4000 N.
  (i) Calculate the modulus of elasticity of the spring.
  (ii) If the spring were cut into two equal parts, what would be the stiffness of each part?

The weight of a car is 8000 N and half of this weight is taken by two such 10-coil front springs so that each bears a load of 2000 N.
  (iii) Find the compression of each spring.
  (iv) Two people each of weight 800 N get into the front of the car. How much further are the springs compressed? (Assume that their weight is carried equally by the front springs.)

3 The coach of an impoverished rugby club decides to construct a scrummaging machine as illustrated in the diagrams below. It is to consist of a vertical board, supported in horizontal runners at the top and bottom of each end. The board is held away from the wall by springs, as shown, and the players push the board with their shoulders, against the thrust of the springs.

The coach has one spring of length 1.4 m and stiffness 5000 Nm^{-1}, which he cuts into two pieces of equal length.

(i) Find the modulus of elasticity of the original spring.

(ii) Find the modulus of elasticity and the stiffness of each of the half-length springs.

(iii) On one occasion the coach observes that the players compress the springs by 20 cm. What total force do they produce in the forward direction?

4 The diagram shows the rear view of a load of weight 300 N in the back of a pick-up truck of width 2 m.

The load is 1.2 m wide, 0.8 m high and is situated centrally on the truck. The coefficient of friction between the load and the truck is 0.4. The load is held down by an elastic rope of natural length 2 m and modulus of elasticity 400 N which may be assumed to pass smoothly over the corners and across the top of the load. The rope is secured at the edges of the truck platform. Find

(i) the tension in the rope

(ii) the normal reaction of the truck on the load

(iii) the percentage by which the maximum possible frictional force is increased by using the rope

(iv) the shortest stopping distance for which the load does not slide, given that the truck is travelling at 30 ms^{-1} initially. (Assume constant deceleration and use 10 for g.)

5 Two springs of stiffness k_1 and k_2 are connected in series as shown and a force F is applied to each end.

$$F \longleftarrow \overset{k_1}{\text{00000000000000}} \sim \overset{k_2}{\text{00000000000000}} \longrightarrow F$$

(i) Write down the tension in each spring and find expressions for their extensions in terms of F, k_1 and k_2.

(ii) If these two springs are equivalent to one spring of stiffness k show that:

$$\frac{1}{k} = \frac{1}{k_1} + \frac{1}{k_2}$$

The two springs (which are of the same length) are now connected in parallel, and held so that their extensions are equal.

(iii) Show that they are now equivalent to a spring with stiffness $k_1 + k_2$.

6 The diagram shows two light springs, AP and BP, connected at P. The ends A and B are secured firmly and the system is in equilibrium.

The spring AP has natural length 1 m and modulus of elasticity 16 N.
The spring BP has natural length 1.2 m and modulus of elasticity 30 N.
The distance AB is 2.5 m and the extension of the spring AP is x m.

(i) Write down an expression, in terms of x, for the extension of the spring BP.

(ii) Find expressions, in terms of x, for the tensions in both springs.

(iii) Find the value of x.

7 The diagram shows two light springs, CQ and DQ, connected to a particle, Q, of weight 20 N. The ends C and D are secured firmly and the system is in equilibrium, lying in a vertical line.

The spring CQ has natural length 0.8 m and modulus of elasticity 16 N; DQ has natural length 1.2 m and modulus of elasticity 36 N. The distance CD is 3 m and QD is h m.

(i) Write down expressions, in terms of h, for the extensions of the two springs.

(ii) Find expressions, in terms of h, for the tensions in the two springs.

(iii) Use these results to find the value of h.

(iv) Find the forces the system exerts at C and at D.

8 The diagram shows a block of wood of mass m lying on a plane inclined at an angle α to the horizontal. The block is attached to a fixed peg by means of a light elastic string of natural length l_0 and modulus of elasticity λ; the string lies parallel to the line of greatest slope. The block is in equilibrium.

Find the extension of the string in the following cases.

(i) The plane is smooth.

(ii) The coefficient of friction between the plane and the block is μ ($\mu \neq 0$) and the block is about to slide **(a)** up the plane **(b)** down the plane.

9 In this question take g to be $10\,\text{ms}^{-2}$. A baby bouncer consists of a light, inextensible harness attached to a spring. It is suspended in a doorway on the end of a chain so that the baby's feet just touch the floor. The baby can then use its feet to bounce up and down. One such harness, with a spring of natural length 20 cm, is set up for Emily (who has mass 10 kg). Before Emily is put into the harness (i.e. when the spring is not extended) the bottom of the harness is 17 cm from the ground. When she sits in the harness with her feet off the ground, the bottom of the harness is 15 cm above the ground.

(i) Find the modulus of elasticity of the spring.

The baby bouncer is also used by Charlotte and its height is not adjusted for her. Charlotte's mass is 12 kg (the limit recommended for the bouncer).

(ii) What is the extension of the spring when Charlotte sits in the bouncer with her feet off the ground?

(iii) Charlotte sits in equilibrium with her feet on the ground.
Find an expression for the reaction, R N, between her feet and the ground in terms of the height, h cm, of the harness above the ground.

10 A strong elastic band of natural length 1 m and modulus of elasticity 12 N is stretched round two pegs P and Q which are in a horizontal line a distance 1 m apart. A bag of mass 1.5 kg is hooked on to the band at H and hangs in equilibrium so that PH and QH make angles of θ with the horizontal. Make the modelling assumptions that the elastic band is light and runs smoothly over the pegs.

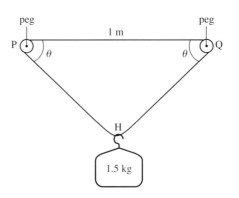

(i)   Use Hooke's law to show that the tension in the band is $12\sec\theta$.

(ii)   Find the depth of the hook below the horizontal line PQ.

(iii)   Is the modelling in this question realistic?

11 A light spring AB has natural length 0.8 m and modulus of elasticity 200 N. The end A is fixed and a small ball is attached at B. The ball hangs in equilibrium below A.

(i)   Given that the length of the spring is 1 metre, calculate the mass of the ball.

(ii)   If instead the mass of the ball is 2 kg, calculate the length of the spring.

The end A of the spring is now fixed to a vertical wall and the end B is fixed to the mid-point of a light rod CD of length 1.2 m, as shown in the diagram. The end C of the rod is freely hinged to the wall vertically below A and a small ball of mass m kg is attached to the end D of the rod. The rod rests in equilibrium perpendicular to the spring and at an angle of $60°$ to the upward vertical.

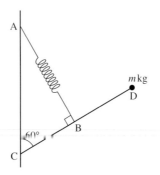

(iii)   Show that the extension of the spring is 0.239 m (correct to 3 significant figures) and hence calculate the tension in the spring.

(iv)   Calculate m.

The end A of the spring is now attached to a different point on the wall. In this position the rod rests horizontally in equilibrium and angle ABC $= \theta$.

(v)   Show that $3\tan\theta - 4\sin\theta = 1.38$, correct to 3 significant figures.

[MEI]

12 Many cafeterias have a device for stacking plates where, for any number of plates in the stack, the top of the top plate is always at the counter level, as shown in the diagram on the left. This is achieved by standing the plates on a metal base which is supported by a number of springs which hang vertically as shown in the diagram on the right. The base is shaped so that when there are no plates on the stack, the top of the base is level with the counter.

The situation may be modelled by assuming that each plate has a mass of 0.1 kg and raises the vertical height of the stack by 1.5 cm when placed on another plate (or the base). The springs have a natural length of 10 cm and a modulus of 0.8 N. The springs may be assumed to be light and resistances to motion due to friction may be neglected.

(i) Suppose that n springs are attached.

    (a) Show that the extension in each spring when a mass m kg is supported by the system is given by $\dfrac{mg}{8n}$ m.

    (b) What is the further extension of each spring when one plate is added to the stack?

(ii) Show that nine springs are required if the addition of each plate allows the top of that plate to be as near to the counter level as possible but above, not below, the counter level.

(iii) Assuming that nine springs are used, approximately how many plates would be above the counter level if there were 40 plates in the stack?

The system can be adjusted so that the top of the plate is at counter level by reducing the natural length of the springs.

(iv) When eight springs are used, what should be the natural length of each spring, correct to three decimal places?

[MEI]

Work and energy

In order to stretch an elastic spring a force must do work on it. In the case of the muscle exerciser, this force is provided by the muscles working against the tension. When the exerciser is pulled at constant speed, at any given time the force F applied at each end is equal to the tension in the spring; consequently it changes as the spring stretches.

Figure 2.6

Suppose that one end of the spring is stationary and the extension is x as in figure 2.7. By Hooke's law the tension is given by

$$T = kx,$$

and so
$$F = kx$$

The work done by a *constant* force F in moving a distance d in its own direction is given by Fd. To find the work done by a *variable* force the process has to be considered in small stages.

Figure 2.7

Now imagine that the force extends the string a small distance δx. The work done is given by $\quad F\delta x = kx\,\delta x.$

The total work done in stretching the spring many small distances is

$$\Sigma F\delta x = \Sigma kx\delta x$$

In the limit as $\delta x \to 0$, the work done is

$$\int F\,dx = \int kx\,dx$$

$$= \tfrac{1}{2}kx^2 + c$$

When the extension $x = 0$, the work done is zero, so $c = 0$.

The total work done in stretching the spring an extension x *from its natural length l_0* is therefore given by:

$$\tfrac{1}{2}kx^2 \quad \text{or} \quad \tfrac{1}{2}\frac{\lambda}{l_0}x^2$$

The result is the same for the work done in compressing a spring.

Elastic potential energy

The tensions and thrusts in perfectly elastic springs and strings are conservative forces, since any work done against them can be recovered in the form of kinetic energy. A catapult and a jack-in-a-box use this property.

Figure 2.8

The work done in stretching or compressing a string or spring can therefore be regarded as potential energy. It is known as *elastic potential energy.*

The elastic potential energy stored in a spring which is stretched or compressed by an amount x is

$$\tfrac{1}{2}kx^2 \quad \text{or} \quad \tfrac{1}{2}\frac{\lambda}{l_0}x^2$$

EXAMPLE 2.4

An elastic rope of natural length 0.6 m is extended to a length of 0.8 m. The modulus of elasticity of the rope is 25 N. Find

(i) the elastic potential energy stored in the rope
(ii) the further energy required to stretch it to a length of 1.65 m over a car roof-rack.

SOLUTION

(i) The extension of the elastic is $(0.8 - 0.6)\,\text{m} = 0.2\,\text{m}$.

The energy stored in the rope is $\frac{1}{2}\frac{\lambda}{l_0}x^2$

$$= \frac{25}{2 \times 0.6}(0.2)^2$$

$$= 0.83\,\text{J (to 2 d.p.)}.$$

(ii) The extension of the elastic rope is now $1.65 - 0.6 = 1.05\,\text{m}$

The elastic energy stored in the rope is $\frac{25}{2 \times 0.6}(1.05)^2$

$$= 22.97\,\text{J}$$

The extra energy required to stretch the rope is $22.14\,\text{J}$ (correct to 2 d.p.).

⚠️ In the example above, the string is stretched so that its extension changes from x_1 to x_2 (in this case, from 0.2 m to 1.05 m). The work required to do this is

$$\tfrac{1}{2}kx_2{}^2 - \tfrac{1}{2}kx_1{}^2 = \tfrac{1}{2}k(x_2{}^2 - x_1{}^2) \text{ or } \tfrac{1}{2}\frac{\lambda}{l_0}(x_2{}^2 - x_1{}^2)$$

You can see by using algebra that this expression is *not* the same as $\frac{1}{2}k(x_2 - x_1)^2$, so it is *not* possible to use the extra extension $(x_2 - x_1)$ directly in the energy expression to calculate the extra energy stored in the string.

EXAMPLE 2.5

A catapult has prongs which are 16 cm apart and the elastic string is 20 cm long. A marble of mass 70 g is placed in the centre of the elastic string and pulled back so that the string is just taut. The marble is then pulled back a further 9 cm and the force required to keep it in this position is 60 N. Find

(i) the stretched length of the string

(ii) the tension in the string and its stiffness

(iii) the elastic potential energy stored in the string and the speed of the marble when the string regains its natural length, assuming they remain in contact.

SOLUTION

To solve this problem it is necessary to assume that there is no elasticity in the frame of the catapult, and that the motion takes place in a horizontal plane. In addition, any air resistance is ignored.

In figure 2.9, A and B are the ends of the elastic string and M_1 and M_2 are the two positions of the marble (before and after the string is stretched). D is the mid-point of AB.

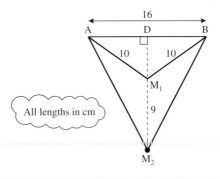

Figure 2.9

(i) Using Pythagoras' theorem in triangle DBM_1 gives

$$DM_1 = \sqrt{10^2 - 8^2} = 6\,\text{cm}.$$

So

$$DM_2 = 9 + 6 = 15\,\text{cm}.$$

Using Pythagoras' theorem in triangle DBM_2 gives

$$BM_2 = \sqrt{15^2 + 8^2} = 17\,\text{cm}$$

The stretched length of the string is $2 \times 17\,\text{cm} = 0.34\,\text{m}$.

(ii) Take the tension in the string to be T N.

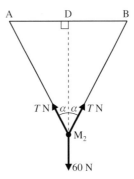

Figure 2.10

Resolving parallel to M_2D

$$2T\cos\alpha = 60$$

Now

$$\cos\alpha = \frac{DM_2}{BM_2} = \frac{0.15}{0.17}$$

so

$$T = 34$$

The extension of the string is $(0.34 - 0.2)\,\text{m} = 0.14\,\text{m}$.

By Hooke's law the stiffness k is given by $kx = T$

$$k = \frac{34}{0.14} = 242.9$$

The stiffness of the string is $240\,\text{Nm}^{-1}$ (to 2 s.f.).

(iii) The elastic potential energy stored in the string is

$$\tfrac{1}{2}kx^2 = \tfrac{1}{2} \times 242.9 \times (0.14)^2 = 2.38\,\mathrm{J}$$

By the principle of conservation of energy, this is equal to the kinetic energy given to the marble. The mass of the marble is 0.07 kg, so

$$\tfrac{1}{2} \times 0.07v^2 = 2.38$$
$$\Rightarrow \quad v = 8.25\ldots$$

The speed of the marble is $8.3\,\mathrm{ms}^{-1}$.

EXERCISE 2C

1 An open coiled spring has natural length 0.3 m and stiffness $20\,\mathrm{Nm}^{-1}$. Find the elastic potential energy in the spring when
  (i) it is extended by 0.1 m
  (ii) it is compressed by 0.01 m
  (iii) its length is 0.5 m
  (iv) its length is 0.3 m.

2 A spring has natural length 0.4 m and modulus of elasticity 20 N. Find the elastic energy stored in the spring when
  (i) it is extended by 0.4 m
  (ii) it is compressed by 0.1 m
  (iii) its length is 0.2 m
  (iv) its length is 0.45 m.

3 A pinball machine fires small balls of mass 50 g by means of a spring and a light plunger. The spring and the ball move in a horizontal plane. The spring has stiffness $600\,\mathrm{Nm}^{-1}$ and is compressed by 5 cm to fire a ball.

  (i) Find the energy stored in the spring immediately before the ball is fired.
  (ii) Find the speed of the ball when it is fired.

4 A catapult is made from elastic string with modulus of elasticity 5 N. The string is attached to two prongs which are 15 cm apart, and is just taut. A pebble of mass 40 g is placed in the centre of the string and is pulled back 4 cm and then released in a horizontal direction.

15 cm

(i) Calculate the work done in stretching the string.

(ii) Calculate the speed of the pebble on leaving the catapult.

5 A simple mathematical model of a railway buffer consists of a horizontal open coiled spring attached to a fixed point. The stiffness of the spring is $10^5 \, \text{Nm}^{-1}$ and its natural length is 2 m.

The buffer is designed to stop a railway truck before the spring is compressed to half its natural length, otherwise the truck will be damaged.

(i) Find the elastic energy stored in the spring when it is half its natural length.

(ii) Find the maximum speed at which a truck of mass 2 tonnes can approach the buffer safely. Neglect any other reasons for loss of energy of the truck.

A truck of mass 2 tonnes approaches the buffer at $5 \, \text{ms}^{-1}$.

(iii) Calculate the minimum length of the spring during the subsequent period of contact.

(iv) Find the thrust in the spring and the acceleration of the truck when the spring is at its minimum length.

(v) What happens next?

6 Two identical springs are attached to a sphere of mass 0.5 kg that rests on a smooth horizontal surface as shown. The other ends of the springs are attached to fixed points A and B.

The springs each have stiffness $30 \, \text{Nm}^{-1}$ and natural length 25 cm. The sphere is at rest at the mid-point when it is projected with speed $2 \, \text{ms}^{-1}$ along the line of the springs towards B. Calculate the length of each spring when the sphere first comes to rest.

7 Two light springs are joined and stretched between two fixed points A and C which are 2 m apart as shown in the diagram. The spring AB has natural length 0.5 m and modulus of elasticity 10 N. The spring BC has natural length 0.6 m and modulus of elasticity 6 N. The system is in equilibrium.

(i) Explain why the tensions in the two springs are the same.

(ii) Find the distance AB and the tension in each spring.

(iii) How much work must be done to stretch the springs from their natural length to connect them as described above?

A small object of mass 0.012 kg is attached at B and is supported on a smooth horizontal table. A, B and C lie in a straight horizontal line and the mass is released from rest at the mid-point of AC.

(iv) What is the speed of the mass when it passes through the equilibrium position of the system?

[MEI]

8

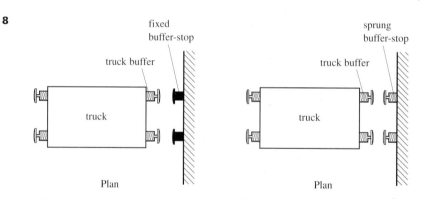

A railway truck of mass 4.5 tonnes, travelling with a speed of $0.5\,\mathrm{ms}^{-1}$, collides with a *fixed* buffer-stop, as indicated in the diagram on the left.

The truck itself has, at each end, two buffers of negligible mass, each of which may be modelled as a spring of stiffness $25\,000\,\mathrm{Nm}^{-1}$. The truck comes momentarily to rest with the buffers compressed by a distance x cm and you may neglect the work done against any forces other than those in the buffers.

(i) Calculate the kinetic energy of the truck immediately before the impact.

(ii) Calculate the value of x.

The truck's buffers are designed to be compressed by up to 24 cm.

(iii) Calculate the greatest speed of the truck if it can be brought momentarily to rest by compression of the buffers.

On another occasion the same truck is travelling at 0.8 ms^{-1} when it collides with a *sprung* buffer-stop, as indicated in the diagram on the right. The sprung buffer-stop has two buffers, each of which makes contact with a buffer on the truck. Each buffer on the buffer-stop has negligible mass and may be modelled by a spring of stiffness 20 000 Nm^{-1}. The truck is brought momentarily to rest when its buffers are compressed by a distance x_1 m and those of the stop by a distance of x_2 m. You may assume that the forces of compression in each spring are equal in magnitude when the truck comes momentarily to rest.

(iv) Write down two equations involving x_1 and x_2 and hence determine their values.

[MEI]

9 A light elastic band is made from a piece of elastic of total natural length $2a$ (i.e. it is of length a when lying naturally).

The band is hung vertically over a small, smooth peg. When a mass m is attached to the bottom of the band its length is trebled.

(i) Show that the modulus of elasticity is $\dfrac{mg}{4}$.

The band is now stretched over two small, smooth pegs a distance $2a$ apart in a horizontal line. The mass m is fixed to the centre of the lower strand of the band and gently lowered to a position in which the mass is a distance $2a$ below the line of the pegs, as shown in the diagram.

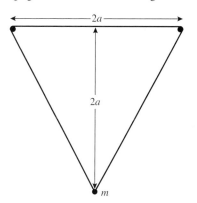

(ii) Calculate the extension in the band.
(iii) Show that the mass hangs in equilibrium in this position.
(iv) How much energy is given to the band while the mass is being lowered?
(v) Why is your answer to part (iv) not equal to the potential energy lost by the mass on being lowered?

[MEI]

10 The end A of a light elastic string AB is fixed to a smooth horizontal table. A small bead of mass 0.05 kg is attached to the end B. Also attached to the end B is another light elastic string BC. The end C is fixed to a point on the table so that the strings lie in a horizontal straight line with the bead resting in equilibrium on the table and with AC equal to 2.3 metres, as shown in the diagram.

The string AB has natural length 0.4 m and modulus of elasticity 4 N. The string BC has natural length 0.5 m and modulus of elasticity 2 N.

(i) The extension in AB is x_1 m and the extension in BC is x_2 m. Show that $5x_1 = 2x_2$ and calculate x_1 and x_2.

The bead is held at A and released.

(ii) Determine whether the string BC goes slack.

(iii) Calculate the maximum extension of the string AB.

[MEI]

Vertical motion

This chapter began with a bungee jumper undergoing vertical motion at the end of an elastic rope. The next example involves a particle in vertical motion at the end of a spring. This, along with the questions in the following exercise, covers the essential work involved in modelling the bungee jump, which you are then invited to investigate.

EXAMPLE 2.6

A particle of mass 0.2 kg is attached to the end A of a perfectly elastic spring OA which has natural length 0.5 m and stiffness 40 Nm^{-1}. The spring is suspended from O and the particle is pulled down and released from rest when the length of the spring is 0.7 m. In the subsequent motion the extension of the spring is denoted by x m.

(i) Write down expressions for the increase in the particle's gravitational potential energy and the decrease in the energy stored in the spring when the extension is x m.

(ii) Hence find an expression for the speed of the particle in terms of x.

(iii) Calculate the length of the spring when the particle is at its highest point.

SOLUTION

(i)

Figure 2.11

The particle has risen a distance $(0.2 - x)$ m

$$\text{Increase in gravitational P.E.} = mgh$$
$$= 1.96 \times (0.2 - x)$$

$$\text{Stored energy} = \tfrac{1}{2}kx^2$$
$$= 20x^2$$

$$\text{Initial stored energy} = 20 \times 0.2^2$$

$$\text{Decrease in stored energy} = 20(0.2^2 - x^2)$$

(ii) The initial K.E. is zero.

$$\text{Increase in K.E.} = \tfrac{1}{2} \times 0.2 \times \dot{x}^2 - 0$$
$$= 0.1\dot{x}^2$$

> $\dot{x}$ is the same as v, the speed in the positive direction

Using the law of conservation of mechanical energy,

$$\text{Increase in K.E.} + \text{P.E.} = \text{Decrease in stored energy}$$

$$0.1\dot{x}^2 + 1.96(0.2 - x) = 20(0.2^2 - x^2)$$

and so
$$v = \dot{x} = \sqrt{200(0.2^2 - x^2) - 19.6(0.2 - x)}$$

(iii) At the highest point, $v = \dot{x} = 0$,

$$200(0.2^2 - x^2) - 19.6(0.2 - x) = 0$$
$$(0.2 - x)[200(0.2 + x) - 19.6] = 0$$
$$\Rightarrow \qquad x = 0.2 \text{ or } 40 + 200x = 19.6$$
$$\Rightarrow \qquad x = 0.2 \text{ or } x = -0.102$$
$$\text{but} \qquad x = 0.2 \text{ at the lowest position}$$
$$\text{so} \qquad x = -0.102 \text{ at the highest point}$$

This negative value of x indicates a compression rather than an extension, so at its highest point the spring has length $(0.5 - 0.102)$ m $= 0.398$ m.

Note

For this question it is important that you are dealing with a spring, which still obeys Hooke's law when it contracts, rather than a string which becomes slack.

1 A particle of mass 0.2 kg is attached to one end of a light elastic spring of stiffness $10\,\mathrm{Nm}^{-1}$. The system hangs vertically and the particle is released from rest when the spring is at its natural length. The particle comes to rest when it has fallen a distance h m.

(i) Write down an expression in terms of h for the energy stored in the spring when the particle comes to rest at its lowest point.

(ii) Write down an expression in terms of h for the gravitational potential energy lost by the particle when it comes to rest at its lowest point.

(iii) Find the value of h.

2 A particle of mass m is attached to one end of a light vertical spring of natural length l_0 and modulus of elasticity $2mg$. The particle is released from rest when the spring is at its natural length. Find, in terms of l_0, the maximum length of the spring in the subsequent motion.

3 A block of mass m is placed on a smooth plane inclined at $30°$ to the horizontal. The block is attached to the top of the plane by a spring of natural length l_0 and modulus λ. The system is released from rest with the spring at its natural length. Find an expression for the maximum length of the spring in the subsequent motion.

4 A particle of mass 0.1 kg is attached to one end of a spring of natural length 0.3 m and modulus of elasticity 20 N. The other end is attached to a fixed point and the system hangs vertically. The particle is released from rest when the length of the spring is 0.2 m. In the subsequent motion the extension of the spring is denoted by x m.

(i) Show that
$$0.05\dot{x}^2 + \frac{10}{0.3}(x^2 - 0.1^2) - 0.98(x + 0.1) = 0$$

(ii) Find the maximum value of x.

5 A small apple of mass 0.1 kg is attached to one end of an elastic string of natural length 25 cm and modulus of elasticity 5 N. David is asleep under a tree and Sam fixes the free end of the string to the branch of the tree just above David's head. Sam releases the apple level with the branch and it just touches David's head in the subsequent motion. How high above his head is the branch?

6 A block of mass 0.5 kg lies on a light scale pan which is supported on a vertical spring of natural length 0.4 m and modulus of elasticity 40 N. Initially the spring is at its natural length and the block is moving downwards with a speed of $2\,\mathrm{ms}^{-1}$. Gravitational potential energy is measured relative to the initial position and g should be taken to be $10\,\mathrm{ms}^{-2}$.

(i) Find the initial mechanical energy of the system.

(ii) Show that the speed $v\,\mathrm{ms}^{-1}$ of the block when the compression of the spring is x m is given by $v = 2\sqrt{1 + 5x - 50x^2}$.

(iii) Find the minimum length of the spring during the oscillations.

7   A scale pan of mass 0.5 kg is suspended from a fixed point by a spring of stiffness $500 \, \text{Nm}^{-1}$ and natural length 10 cm.

   (i) Calculate the length of the spring when the scale pan is in equilibrium.

   (ii) A bag of sugar of mass 1 kg is gently placed on the pan and the system is released from rest. Find the maximum length of the spring in the subsequent motion.

8   A bungee jump is carried out by a person of mass m kg using an elastic rope which can be taken to obey Hooke's law. It is known that the jump operator does not exceed the total length limit of four times the original length of the rope in any jump. Prove that the tension in the rope is at most $\frac{8}{3} mg$ N.

9   A conical pendulum consists of a bob of mass m attached to an inextensible string of length l. The bob describes a circle of radius r with angular speed ω, and the string makes an angle θ with the vertical as shown.

   (i) Find an expression for θ in terms of ω, l and g.

   The string is replaced with an elastic string of stiffness k and natural length l_0.

   (ii) Find an expression for the new value of θ in terms of ω, m, g, l_0 and k.

10 A light, elastic string has natural length 0.5 m and modulus of elasticity 49 N. The end A is attached to a point on a ceiling. A small object of mass 3 kg is attached to the end B of the string and hangs in equilibrium.

   (i) Calculate the length AB.

   A second string, identical to the first one, is now attached to the object at B and to a point C on the floor, 2.5 m vertically below the point A. The system is in equilibrium with B a distance x m below A, as shown in the diagram below.

(ii) Find the tension in each of the strings in terms of x and hence show that $x = 1.4$.

(iii) Calculate the total elastic potential energy in the strings when the object hangs in equilibrium.

The object is now pulled down 0.1 m from its equilibrium position and released from rest.

(iv) Calculate the speed of the object when it passes through the equilibrium position. Any resistances to motion may be neglected.

[**MEI**]

11 A light elastic string AB has stiffness k and natural length l_0.

The end A of the string is fixed to a vertical wall, and the end B to a block of mass M which is supported by a smooth horizontal plane. To the other side of the block is attached an inelastic light string which passes over a smooth pulley and is then tied to a particle of mass m at C which hangs freely at all times. The block is initially held against the wall and then is moved gently towards the pulley until it is in equilibrium. The elastic string and the part of the other string between the block and the pulley are horizontal, as shown in the diagram below.

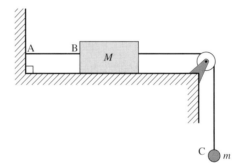

Find expressions for the following in terms of some or all of m, g, k and l_0.

(i) The extension in the elastic string.

(ii) The potential energy lost by the hanging mass as the system is moved to its equilibrium position.

(iii) The energy stored in the elastic string.

(iv) Compare your answers to parts (ii) and (iii). Why is energy not conserved?

(v) If the string supporting the hanging mass breaks when the system is in equilibrium, show that the block will hit the wall with a speed v given by $v^2 = \dfrac{m^2 g^2}{Mk}$. Find also an expression for the acceleration of the block immediately after the string breaks.

[**MEI**]

12 A man unloading 25 kg sacks drops each one 2 m, from rest, on to a light horizontal sprung board which breaks the fall. The spring supporting the board is initially 50 cm long and compresses down to a minimum length of 15 cm under the impact of each falling sack which is then removed by another man.

Assuming that there is no energy loss on impact,

(i) show that the potential energy lost by the sack when it reaches its lowest point is about 576 J

(ii) show that the stiffness of the spring is 9400 Nm^{-1}

(iii) find the maximum deceleration experienced by the falling sack.

[MEI]

13 A child suspends a small model aeroplane from the ceiling by means of a light elastic string of modulus 5 N and natural length 0.8 m. The aeroplane is packed with some modelling clay and the total mass is 0.1 kg.

(i) Calculate the length of the string when the aeroplane hangs in equilibrium.

(ii) The aeroplane is pulled vertically down until the string is 1.2 m long and then released from rest. Calculate the minimum distance between the aeroplane and the ceiling in the resulting motion.

The child wishes the aeroplane to hang 0.9 m below the ceiling when in equilibrium. The child considers two possibilities. The first possibility is to remove some of the clay.

(iii) What mass of clay would need to be removed?

The other possibility is not to remove any clay, but instead to shorten the string to a new natural length.

(iv) What would the new natural length need to be?

The child again holds the aeroplane 1.2 m below the ceiling and releases it from rest.

(v) Explain, without doing any calculations, whether the aeroplane will get closer to the ceiling than in part (ii)

   (a) if clay has been removed as in part (iii)

   (b) if the string has been shortened as in part (iv).

[MEI]

The bungee jump

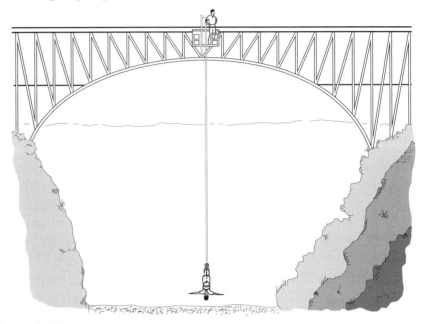

Figure 2.12

(i) *Experiment*

Use a weight to represent the jumper and a piece of elastic for the bungee. Measure l_0 and find the value of λ by suspending the weight in equilibrium. Try to predict the lowest point reached by the weight when it is dropped. Can you estimate a suitable length of elastic for any given weight to fall a standard height?

(ii) *Modelling*

Typical parameters for a mobile crane bungee jump of the type usually done in Britain are:

Height of jump station: 55 m
Bottom safety space: 5 m
Static line length: 5 m (non-elastic straps etc.)
Unstretched elastic rope length: 12 m
Modulus of elasticity: 1000 N

 Calculate the maximum deceleration of the heaviest person who can jump safely. Would a lighter person experience a greater or lesser deceleration?

❓ In practice, bungee jumpers usually use a braided rope. The braiding not only keeps the elastic core stretched, it also prevents the rope from stretching too much. As the rope begins to approach its maximum length, the modulus of elasticity gradually increases until 'lock out' occurs at maximum extension. This rope then no longer obeys Hooke's law. How would the jump feel different using a braided rope?

KEY POINTS

1 **Hooke's law**

The tension T in an elastic string or spring and its extension x are related by:

$$T = kx \quad \text{or} \quad T = \frac{\lambda}{l_0}x$$

where k is the stiffness, λ is the modulus of elasticity and l_0 is the natural length of the string or spring.

2 When a spring is compressed, x is negative and the tension becomes a thrust.

3 **Elastic potential energy**

The elastic potential energy stored in a stretched spring or string, or in a compressed spring, is given by E.P.E. where:

$$\text{E.P.E.} = \tfrac{1}{2}kx^2 \quad \text{or} \quad \text{E.P.E.} = \tfrac{1}{2}\frac{\lambda}{l_0}x^2.$$

This is the work done in stretching a spring or string or compressing a spring starting at its natural length.

4 The tension or thrust in an elastic string or spring is a conservative force and so the elastic potential energy is recoverable.

5 When no frictional or other dissipative forces are involved, elastic potential energy can be used with kinetic energy and gravitational potential energy to form equations using the principle of conservation of energy.

Modelling oscillations

Backwards and forwards half her length
With a short uneasy motion.

Samuel Coleridge Taylor
The Rime of the Ancient Mariner

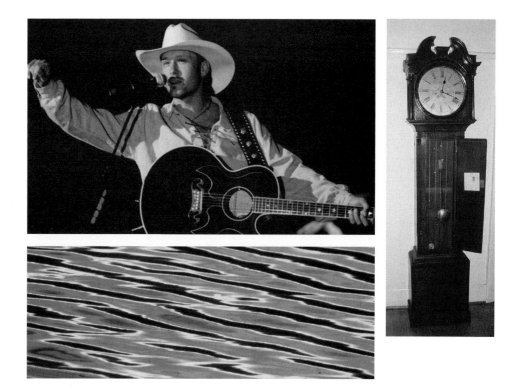

The guitar, the clock and water ripples all involve *oscillations* or *vibrations* of particles or bodies.

- In the guitar, the strings vibrate in a controllable way, and the instrument transmits them as sound waves (vibrations of air molecules).
- In the clock, the pendulum oscillates in the familiar swinging pattern, and this regular motion is used to operate the clock mechanism.
- Ripples are created when the surface of water (or another liquid) is disturbed. The fluid particles vibrate up and down in a regular wave pattern. The same pattern is visible in ocean waves, or in the wakes of boats.

The remarkable thing about all of these vibrations, and many others that occur in natural and man-made systems, is that they are essentially of the same form. The vibrations don't go on for ever, but over a reasonable interval, you can plot the displacement of a vibrating particle against time for any of these systems and you will obtain a sine wave.

Oscillating motion

The graph in figure 3.1 shows the displacement of an oscillating particle against time.

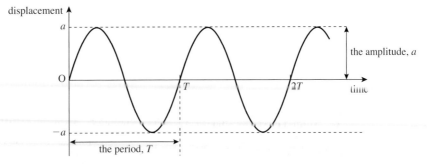

Figure 3.1

From the graph you can see a number of important features of such motion.

- The particle oscillates about a *central position*, O.
- The particle moves between two points with displacements $-a$ and $+a$. The distance a is called the *amplitude* of the motion.
- The motion repeats itself in a cyclic fashion. The number of cycles per second is called the *frequency*, and is usually denoted by v, the Greek letter 'nu'.
- The motion repeats itself after a time T. The time interval T is called the *period*: it is the time for one complete cycle of the motion.

The frequency and period are reciprocals. For example a period of $\frac{1}{10}$ of a second corresponds to a frequency of 10 cycles per second.

Usually the *period* is used when describing relatively slow mechanical oscillations and the *frequency* for faster oscillations or vibrations.

The S.I. unit for frequency is the *hertz* (Hz). One hertz is one cycle per second. The unit is named after Heinrich Rudolph Hertz (1857–94) who was the first person to produce electromagnetic waves artificially. You may be familiar with the use of the *megahertz* (MHz) as a measure of the frequency of radio waves. A radio station which is broadcasting on 99.1 megahertz is producing electromagnetic waves with a frequency of 99 100 000 cycles per second.

Historical note

Pythagoras (572 to 497 BC) studied the pitch of notes produced by stretched strings in the first recorded acoustic experiments. He showed that recognisable musical intervals are produced by segments of a stretched string when their lengths are in a simple numerical ratio.

In May 1939, shortly before the outbreak of the second world war, an international conference in London unanimously agreed to adopt a frequency of '440 cycles per second for the note 'A' in the treble clef'. There are then standard relationships between this and the frequencies of other notes. For many years, before electronic music making devices became readily available, an 'A' of this frequency was broadcast regularly on the radio for the use of musicians.

A physical model of an oscillating system

A particle, P, of mass m kg is attached to a light, perfectly elastic spring which has stiffness $k\,\mathrm{Nm}^{-1}$. The other end, E, of the spring is attached to a fixed point and P moves horizontally.

? How can this be done so that the only horizontal force is the force in the spring?

The spring is its natural length when P is at the fixed point O. The particle is pulled aside to a point A where OA $= a$ m and let go.

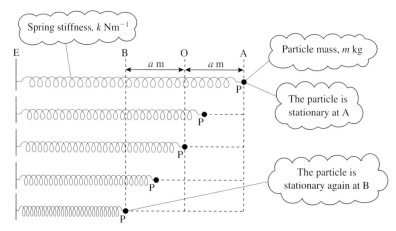

Figure 3.2

? What happens to P as it moves from A to B? Then what happens?

? If you could fix a pen at P and let it draw on a strip of paper moving at a steady rate perpendicular to EA (up the page), what would be the result?

Now think about energy. At A, the spring has elastic energy $\frac{1}{2}ka^2$ and the particle has zero kinetic energy. The particle first comes to rest again at B so the elastic energy at B must also be $\frac{1}{2}ka^2$ and the length OB a m. This is the amplitude of the motion.

When the extension of the spring is x m and P has speed $v\,\mathrm{ms}^{-1}$, the total energy is $\frac{1}{2}mv^2 + \frac{1}{2}kx^2$ so the principle of conservation of energy gives

$$\tfrac{1}{2}mv^2 + \tfrac{1}{2}kx^2 = \tfrac{1}{2}ka^2$$
$$\Rightarrow \quad v^2 = \frac{k}{m}(a^2 - x^2)$$

This gives the speed of the particle in any position, even when x is negative, providing Hooke's law still holds.

? What is its speed at O? What is its maximum speed?

A mathematical model for simple harmonic motion

At the instant the particle, P, is x m to the right of O the forces acting on it are as shown in figure 3.3.

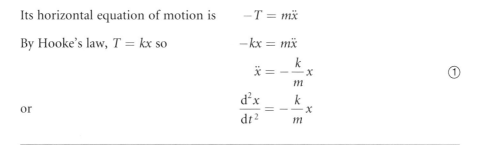

Figure 3.3

Its horizontal equation of motion is

$$-T = m\ddot{x}$$

By Hooke's law, $T = kx$ so

$$-kx = m\ddot{x}$$

$$\ddot{x} = -\frac{k}{m}x \qquad \text{①}$$

or

$$\frac{\mathrm{d}^2 x}{\mathrm{d}t^2} = -\frac{k}{m}x$$

? What is the effect of the minus sign in this equation?

In equation ①, k and m are both positive constants so $\dfrac{k}{m}$ can be written as one positive constant. By convention this is denoted by ω^2 so the equation may be written as

> Writing it as a square ensures that it is always positive.

$$\ddot{x} = -\omega^2 x \qquad \text{②}$$

The equation for the velocity that you found in the last section can then be written as

$$v^2 = \omega^2(a^2 - x^2) \quad \text{or} \quad \dot{x}^2 = \omega^2(a^2 - x^2) \qquad \text{③}$$

You will find how equation ③ can be derived directly from equation ② in the Mathematical notes on page 187.

? What is v when $x = a$, $-a$ and 0?

There are many other similar systems which produce an equation of the same form as equation ②. Because the same equation of motion applies to all of them they all have the same type of oscillating motion called *simple harmonic motion* (SHM).

Simple harmonic motion is defined by the equation $\ddot{x} = -\omega^2 x$. Remember that in this equation, $\ddot{x}$ means acceleration and x means the displacement from the centre. It may be stated in words as

> The acceleration is proportional to the magnitude of the displacement from the centre point of the motion and is directed towards this centre point.

The two equations $v^2 = \omega^2(a^2 - x^2)$ and $\ddot{x} = -\omega^2 x$ tell you a lot about the motion.

From the first equation you can see that

- the motion is symmetrical about the point O where $x = 0$
- x must always lie between $-a$ and a, otherwise v^2 would be negative
- at the extreme points, when $x = \pm a$, the velocity is zero
- the maximum speed is when $x = 0$ and $v = \pm a\omega$.

> This is when the particle passes through O

The second equation tells you that

- $\ddot{x}$ is always directed towards O, so the same must be true of the resultant force
- $\ddot{x}$ and hence the force are zero when $x = 0$, so O is the equilibrium position
- $\ddot{x}$ has a maximum magnitude of $\omega^2 a$ when $x = \pm a$.

These results for $\ddot{x}$ and v in terms of x are shown in the diagram.

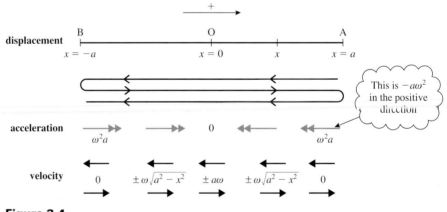

> This is $-a\omega^2$ in the positive direction

Figure 3.4

The frequency of the motion depends on the value of ω. In the next section on page 93 you will see how to write x, v and $\ddot{x}$ in terms of time. In the meantime you can use the result

$$\omega = 2\pi \times \text{frequency}$$

EXAMPLE 3.1

When a violin string is playing an 'A' with frequency 880 Hz, a particle on the string oscillates with amplitude of 0.5 mm. Calculate

(i) the time taken for one complete oscillation
(ii) ω in terms of π and write down the equation of motion
(iii) the maximum speed of the particle and its maximum acceleration
(iv) the acceleration and velocity when the particle is 0.25 mm from its central position.

SOLUTION

(i) The particle does 880 oscillations per second, so the time for one oscillation is $\frac{1}{880} = 0.001\,13$ s. This is the period of the motion.

(ii) $$\omega = 2\pi \times \text{frequency} = 1760\pi$$

The equation of motion is $\qquad \ddot{x} = -\omega^2 x$

$$\Rightarrow \qquad \ddot{x} = -(1760\pi)^2 x$$

(iii) You can use the equations with mm so long as your units are consistent.

Maximum speed $\qquad a\omega = 0.5 \times 1760\pi \;(\text{mm s}^{-1})$

$$= 2.76 \text{ ms}^{-1} \;(3 \text{ s.f.})$$

Maximum acceleration $\qquad a\omega^2 = 0.5 \times (1760\pi)^2 \;(\text{mm s}^{-1})$

$$= 15\,300 \text{ ms}^{-2} \;(3 \text{ s.f.})$$

(iv) When $x = 0.25$, $\qquad \ddot{x} = -(1760\pi)^2 \times 0.25 \;(\text{mm s}^{-2})$

$$\Rightarrow \qquad \text{acceleration} = -7640 \text{ ms}^{-2} \;(3 \text{ s.f.})$$

The velocity is given by $\qquad v^2 = \omega^2(0.5^2 - x^2)$

$$\Rightarrow \qquad v = \pm 1760\pi \sqrt{0.25 - 0.0625} \;(\text{mm s}^{-1})$$

$$\Rightarrow \qquad \text{velocity} = \pm 2.39 \text{ ms}^{-1}$$

the particle can be travelling in either direction

When $x = -0.25$ $\qquad \ddot{x} = +(1760\pi)^2 \times 0.25 \;(\text{mm s}^{-2})$

$$\Rightarrow \qquad \text{acceleration} = +7640 \text{ ms}^{-2}$$

The velocity is $\pm 2.39 \text{ ms}^{-1}$ as before.

In all these questions assume that time is measured in seconds.

1 Write down the equation of motion in the following cases of simple harmonic motion. Calculate for each
  (a) the velocity and magnitude of the acceleration at the centre of the motion
  (b) the velocity and magnitude of the acceleration at the ends of the motion
  (c) the speed when x is half the amplitude.
      (i) $\omega = 3$, amplitude $= 2$ cm
      (ii) $\omega = 10$, amplitude $= 0.1$ m
      (iii) $\omega = \pi$, amplitude $= a$ m.

2 A particle of dust lands at a point A on a surface which is vibrating vertically with SHM centre O and $\omega = 20$. The particle cannot stay in contact with the surface when the downwards acceleration is greater than g. How far (in cm) is the particle from O when this happens? Is it above or below O?

3 A particle is moving with SHM with $\omega = 2$. Initially it is 10 cm from the centre of the motion and moving in the positive direction with a speed of 6 cm s^{-1}. Write down the equation of motion and calculate
  (i) the amplitude
  (ii) the acceleration at the ends of the motion
  (iii) the speed at the centre
  (iv) the speed when it is 5 cm from the centre
  (v) the distance from the centre when the speed is half its maximum.

4 Musical notes which are an octave apart have frequencies in the ratio $1 : 2$. The note A above middle C has a frequency of 440 Hz. On a full-size keyboard there are 4 'A's below it and 3 above it (the range on the keyboard is just over 7 octaves).
  (i) Work out the values of ω corresponding to the frequencies of these seven 'A's.
  (ii) Find the maximum speed of points on piano strings which are vibrating with amplitude 1 mm to produce the highest and lowest of these notes.

5 A loudspeaker cone sounding a pure note of frequency 2000 Hz is modelled by SHM of amplitude 2 mm.
  (i) Calculate ω and the maximum speed of the cone.
  (ii) Write down the equation of motion and calculate the maximum acceleration.

6 A piston in an engine oscillates with a period of 0.03 s and an amplitude of 0.35 m. Modelling the oscillations as SHM,
  (i) draw a sketch graph to illustrate the oscillations
  (ii) calculate the frequency of the motion and hence find ω
  (iii) calculate the maximum speed of the piston.

7 Air sickness might be caused by the rhythmic vibrations of an aircraft. It has been observed that about 50% of the passengers of an aircraft suffer air sickness when it bounces up and down with a frequency of about 0.3 Hz and a maximum acceleration of 4 ms^{-2}. Assuming SHM find

(i) ω and hence the amplitude of the motion

(ii) the greatest vertical speed during this motion.

8 A jig-saw operates at 3000 strokes per minute with the tip of the blade moving 17 mm from the top to the bottom of a stroke. (One stroke is a complete cycle.) Assuming that the motion is simple harmonic, find
   (i)   the maximum speed of the blade
   (II) the maximum acceleration of the blade
   (iii) the speed of the blade when it is 6 mm from the central position.

9 The wave forms of two notes of music, P and Q, are shown below.

   Which of the following statements are true?
   (i)   P is lower than Q.
   (ii) P is louder than Q.
   (iii) The frequency of P is twice that of Q.
   (iv) The period of P is twice that of Q.
   (v)   The amplitude of Q is larger than that of P.

10 A particle is oscillating with SHM.
    Find expressions in terms of a and ω for
    (i) its speed when it is a distance $\dfrac{a}{4}$ from the centre
    (ii) its distance from the centre when its speed is half its maximum speed.

Simple harmonic motion as a function of time

The Mathematical notes on page 187 show you how to integrate the SHM equation so that you can write x, $\dot{x}$, and $\ddot{x}$ in terms of the time, but you can also demonstrate how the SHM equation can be satisfied by certain trigonometrical functions as in the next example.

⚠ Remember that all the angles must be in radians when you use calculus.

EXAMPLE 3.2

(i) Show that $x = 10\sin 3t$ satisfies the simple harmonic motion equation

$$\ddot{x} = -9x$$

(ii) Sketch the graph of $x = 10\sin 3t$ and deduce the amplitude, period and frequency of this motion.

(iii) Verify that $\dot{x}^2 = v^2 = \omega^2(a^2 - x^2)$

(iv) Show that $x = 25\sin 3t$ also satisfies $\ddot{x} = -9x$ and comment on this result.

SOLUTION

(i) $x = 10\sin3t$

Differentiating with respect to t to find the velocity and acceleration:

$$v = \dot{x} = 30\cos3t \qquad \text{①}$$
$$\text{and} \quad \ddot{x} = -90\sin3t$$
$$\Rightarrow \quad \ddot{x} = -9x \qquad \text{②}$$

This is the SHM equation given in the question.

(ii) The graph of the function is shown below.

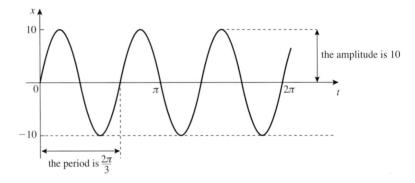

Figure 3.5

The graph shows that the value of x always lies between -10 and 10, so the amplitude of the motion is 10 units.

Each cycle repeats in the time $\dfrac{2\pi}{3}$ so the period of the oscillations, denoted by T, is $\dfrac{2\pi}{3}$. The frequency, f, is $\dfrac{1}{T}$ or $\dfrac{3}{2\pi}$.

(iii) From ①

$$\dot{x}^2 = 900\cos^2 3t$$
$$= 900(1 - \sin^2 3t)$$
$$= 9(100 - 100\sin^2 3t)$$
$$= \omega^2(a^2 - x^2)$$

$\omega^2 = 9$ from equation ②

(iv) Differentiating the function $x = 25\sin3t$ twice gives:

$$\dot{x} = 75\cos3t$$
$$\ddot{x} = -225\sin 3t$$
$$= -9(25\sin3t)$$
$$\Rightarrow \quad \ddot{x} = -9x \text{ as required}$$

This shows that the amplitude of the oscillation is not determined by the differential equation. In this case it can be 10 or 25, or indeed have any other value.

A general form of SHM

Any motion given by an equation of the form $x = a\sin\omega t$ (where a and ω are positive constants) has a similar displacement–time graph and represents SHM with amplitude a. Differentiating this equation gives:

$$v = \dot{x} = a\omega\cos\omega t$$
$$\text{and} \quad \ddot{x} = -a\omega^2\sin\omega t = -\omega^2 x.$$

Figure 3.6 shows how the graphs for x, $\dot{x}$ and $\ddot{x}$ are related.

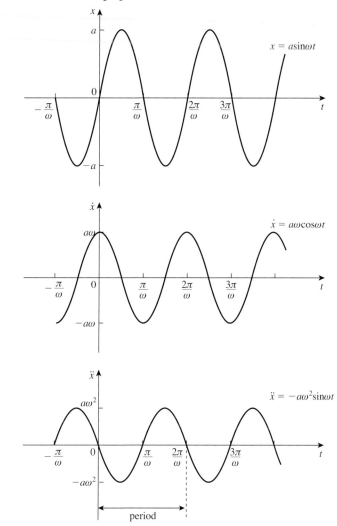

Figure 3.6

The period is shown in figure 3.6, but it can also be found from the equations for x, $\dot{x}$, and $\ddot{x}$. Since $\sin(\omega t + 2\pi) = \sin\omega t$ and $\cos(\omega t + 2\pi) = \cos\omega t$ the values of x, $\dot{x}$, and $\ddot{x}$ remain unchanged when ωt is increased by 2π. This is the smallest increment for which this is true. Also $(\omega t + 2\pi) = \omega\left(t + \dfrac{2\pi}{\omega}\right)$, so whenever you start measuring, all aspects of the motion will be the same after a period of time $T = \dfrac{2\pi}{\omega}$.

In general, $x = a\sin\omega t$ represents SHM with the following properties.

- The amplitude is a (>0)
- The period T is $\dfrac{2\pi}{\omega}$
- The frequency $f = \dfrac{1}{T} = \dfrac{\omega}{2\pi}$
- $x = 0$ when $t = 0$

? Show that the equation $x = a\cos\omega t$ also satisfies the definition of SHM. Draw sketches of the graphs of $x = a\sin\omega t$ and $x = a\cos\omega t$ and compare the properties of the motions represented by them.

Phase difference

For $x = a\cos\omega t$, $x = a$ when $t = 0$. Its graph $x = a\cos\omega t$ is a translation of the graph of $x = a\sin\omega t$ along the t axis by a displacement of $-\dfrac{\pi}{2}\left(\text{or } \dfrac{3\pi}{2}, \dfrac{7\pi}{2} \text{ etc.}\right)$.

Both equations describe SHM but their oscillations are at a different stage in the cycle when $t = 0$.

They are said to have a *phase difference* of $-\dfrac{\pi}{2}\left(\text{or } \dfrac{3\pi}{2} \text{ etc.}\right)$

⚠ Angular frequency

In these mathematical models ωt is an angle; ω is sometimes called the *angular frequency*. It is important to note that, when the model is applied to an oscillating system, ω is a constant which depends on the properties of the system, such as the stiffness of a spring or the length of a pendulum: ω rarely involves a physical angle and, in particular, ω is *not* the angular velocity of the pendulum.

Relationships between acceleration, velocity and displacement

Provided t is measured from an instant when the particle is at the centre and moving in the positive direction, SHM is described by the following equations.

Displacement: $\qquad x = a\sin\omega t$ ①

Velocity: $\qquad v = \dot{x} = a\omega\cos\omega t$ ②

Acceleration: $\qquad \ddot{x} = -a\omega^2\sin\omega t$ ③

It can be seen from equations ① and ③ that

$$\ddot{x} = -\omega^2 x \qquad ④$$

Squaring equation ② gives:

$$v^2 = \dot{x}^2 = a^2\omega^2\cos^2\omega t$$
$$= \omega^2(a^2 - a^2\sin^2\omega t).$$

Therefore $\qquad v^2 = \omega^2(a^2 - x^2) \qquad ⑤$

When the velocity is written in terms of t, it is best to denote it by $\dot{x}$ to stress the fact that it is the derivative of x with respect to t.

? You have already shown that $x = a\cos\omega t$ satisfies the equation of motion for SHM. Now show that $\dot{x}$ satisfies the equation $\dot{x}^2 = \omega^2(a^2 - x^2)$.

EXAMPLE 3.3

In a harbour the cycle of tides can be modelled as SHM with a period of 12 hours 30 minutes. On a certain day high water is 10 m above low water.

(i) Sketch a graph of the height x m of the water above (or below) the mean level against t, the time in hours since the water was at mean level and rising.

(ii) Find a suitable expression to model x in terms of t.

(iii) Determine for how long the water is more than 6 m above the low water mark.

(iv) Find the rate at which the tide is rising or falling when the water is 6 m above the low water mark.

(v) Find the maximum rate at which the tide rises.

SOLUTION

(i)

Figure 3.7

(ii) First find ω and a.

The period of the tide $T = 12.5$ hours.

Since
$$T = \frac{2\pi}{\omega}$$

Since T is in hours, ω is in radians per hour

$$\omega = \frac{2\pi}{T}$$

$$\omega = 0.503$$

From the graph in part (i), the amplitude of the oscillation is 5 m, so $a = 5$.

Since the water has risen x m in t hours after it was at the mean level, a suitable equation is

$$x = a\sin\omega t$$
$$x = 5\sin(0.503t)$$

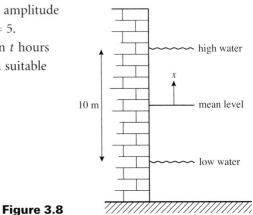

Figure 3.8

(iii) Remember that you are working with time in hours, so any values of t will be in hours. The tide is 6 m above low water when $x \geqslant 1$.

Now $x = 1$ when
$$5\sin(0.503t) = 1$$
$$\Rightarrow \quad \sin(0.503t) = 0.2 = \sin 0.201$$

The first two values of t satisfying this equation are t_1 and t_2 where

$$0.503t_1 = 0.201 \qquad \Rightarrow \quad t_1 = 0.400$$
and
$$0.503t_2 = \pi - 0.201 \qquad \Rightarrow \quad t_2 = 5.846$$

Figure 3.9

The water is 6 m above its lowest level for $(t_2 - t_1)$ hours i.e. about $5\frac{1}{2}$ hours.

(iv) The water is 6 m above its lowest level when $x = 1$. The velocity of the oscillation at this point is given by:

$$v^2 = \omega^2(a^2 - x^2)$$
$$\Rightarrow \quad v = \pm 0.503 \sqrt{25 - 1}$$
$$= \pm 2.46$$

The rate of rise or fall is 2.46 m per hour, or about 4 cm per minute.

(v) Since $v^2 = \omega^2(a^2 - x^2)$, the maximum value of v is $a\omega$ when $x = 0$.

The water is rising fastest at the centre of its motion and the rate at which it is rising is:

$$a\omega = 0.503 \times 5$$
$$= 2.515 \text{ m per hour}$$
$$= 4.2 \text{ cm per minute.}$$

Note

A tidal range of 10 m is large, but is realistic for several places around the British coastline. The rate at which the water is rising, 4.2 cm per minute, does not sound high, but if you think about how fast the water would approach your deck chair up a typical beach (with a gradient of say 3°), you will see that it is quite dramatic.

EXERCISE 3B

1 The diagram illustrates the SHM of a particle.

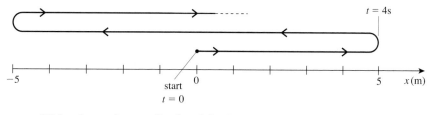

(i) Write down the amplitude of the SHM.

(ii) Write down the period.

(iii) The motion can be described by the equation

$$x = a\sin\omega t$$

Write down the values of a and ω.

(iv) Find

    (a) the displacement

    (b) the velocity

    (c) the acceleration

of the particle when $t = 0$.

2 A particle is performing SHM with five complete cycles per second. At a particular instant it is stationary. It travels 16 cm before it is next stationary.

(i) Write down the period and amplitude of the motion.

(ii) Its motion can be described by the equation $x = a\cos\omega t$. Write down the values of a and ω.

(iii) Use differentiation to find an expression for $\dot{x}$ in terms of t and calculate x and $\dot{x}$ when $t = 0$.

(iv) Find the position and velocity after 0.05 s. In what direction is the particle moving?

3 (i) For SHM with period 2 s and amplitude 2.5 cm, sketch graphs of

(a) displacement (from the central position) against time

(b) velocity against time

(c) acceleration against time.

Line the three graphs up vertically and use the same scale for time in all three.

(ii) All three quantities (displacement, velocity and acceleration) have zero, maximum positive, and maximum negative values. Look at your graphs and state which of these events occur at the same time.

4 A particle is performing SHM with period 12 s and amplitude 2 m. The motion can be described by the equation $x = a\sin\omega t$.

(i) Write down the values of a and ω.

(ii) What distance does the particle travel in the first minute?

(iii) What is its maximum speed?

(iv) Use differentiation to find an expression for the velocity at time t s.

(v) How long after leaving the centre does it take to reach half its maximum speed?

5 A particle is performing SHM described by the equation

$$x = a\sin\omega t$$

Its maximum speed is 10 cm s^{-1} and its period is $\dfrac{\pi}{2}$ s. Lengths are in cm.

(i) Find the values of ω and a.

(ii) Differentiate to find an expression for the velocity $\dot{x}$ and show that $\dot{x}$ is first zero when t is one quarter of the period.

(iii) Find the velocity when t is

(a) 0.2

(b) 1.

In which direction is the particle travelling in each case?

(iv) How far does the particle travel after leaving the central position in

(a) 0.2 s

(b) 1 s.

6 A particle describes SHM with period 12 s and amplitude 10 cm. Initially, $x = 0$.

   (i) Sketch the graph of x against t.

   (ii) Find ω in terms of π and write down a suitable equation for x in terms of t.

   (iii) Find the displacement when $t = 1, 2, 3$.

   (iv) Find the distances travelled during the first, second and third seconds of the motion and explain why they are not equal.

   (v) Give an example of two 1-second intervals during which the particle does travel equal distances.

7 A particle oscillates with SHM, period 8 s and amplitude 10 cm. Time is measured from the instant that the particle is at the end of its motion with x positive. Lengths are in cm.

   (i) Find ω in terms of π and write down a suitable equation for x in terms of t.

   (ii) Differentiate your equation to find an expression for the velocity and calculate the velocity when $t = 0, 1, 2$. Describe the direction of motion in each case.

   (iii) Explain why the speed does not change by equal amounts in equal intervals of time.

8 A particle describes SHM with period 24 s and amplitude 20 cm. Its motion can be described by the equation $x = a\sin\omega t$. Lengths are in cm.

   (i) Write down the values of a and ω and obtain an equation for $\dot{x}$ at time t.

   (ii) Find x and $\dot{x}$ when

     (a) $t = 0$ and

     (b) $t = 2$ and draw a diagram to illustrate the motion in the first 6 s.

   (iii) Find the two smallest values of t for which $x = 10$ and the values of $\dot{x}$ at each of these times.

9 A particle describes SHM with period 24 s and amplitude 20 cm. Its motion can be described by the equation $x = a\cos\omega t$.

   (i) Write down the values of a and ω and obtain an equation for $\dot{x}$ at time t.

   (ii) Find x and $\dot{x}$ when

     (a) $t = 0$

     (b) $t = 2$

   (iii) Draw a diagram to illustrate the motion in the first 6 s.

   (iv) Find the two smallest values of t for which $x = -10\sqrt{3}$ and the values of $\dot{x}$ at each of these times.

10 The top of a piston has a motion which is modelled as simple harmonic with a period of 0.1 s and an amplitude 0.2 m about a mean position A.

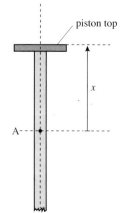

piston top

x

A

(i) Show that x, the displacement of the top of the piston from A after t s, is given by the equation $x = 0.2\sin(20\pi t)$, given that $x = 0$ when $t = 0$.

Where appropriate your answers to the following questions should be expressed in terms of π.

(ii) What is the greatest piston speed?

(iii) What is the greatest magnitude of the acceleration of the piston?

(iv) For what fraction of the period is $x > 0.1$?

[MEI]

11 A small hook moves in a vertical line with displacement y m relative to a fixed point O. The positive sense of y is upwards and the motion of the hook is simple harmonic given by $y = -3\cos 2t$, where the time t is in seconds.

(i) State the amplitude and the period of the simple harmonic motion.

(ii) Find the maximum speed of the hook.

(iii) Find the acceleration of the hook as a function of y.

A light, inextensible string is hung from the hook with a small mass at the lower end. The system starts to move at time $t = 0$.

(iv) How far does the mass move before the string first becomes slack?

(v) At what time does the string first become slack?

[MEI]

12 The motion of a particle is described by the equation $x = 4 + 3\sin\pi t$.

(i) Sketch the graph of the motion and write down its period and amplitude.

(ii) Where is the centre of the oscillations?

(iii) Given that $y = x - 4$, show that $\ddot{y} = -\pi^2 y$

(iv) Find, by further differentiation, an expression for the acceleration, $\ddot{x}$, of the particle at time t.

(v) Describe the motion given by $x = h + a\sin\omega t$.

13 After a boat passes, a duck floating on a river bobs up and down for a short time with SHM period 1 s and amplitude 15 cm. When there is no disturbance, the depth of the water under the duck is 0.5 m.
   (i) What are the greatest and least depths during the motion?
   (ii) Assuming the water rises initially, write down an expression for the depth t seconds after the motion starts.
   (iii) Calculate the first time that the depth is
      (a) 0.55 m   (b) 0.4 m.

14 At a certain location, in a year of 365 days, the latest sunrise is at 8.05 am on 1 January and the earliest is at 3.45 am on 1 July. Sunrise times over a year are to be modelled by a simple harmonic variation of time about a mean time.
   (i) Determine the mean time in minutes after midnight.
   (ii) Find the amplitude of the sunrise variation in minutes.
   (iii) Sketch a graph of sunrise times for a year against day of the year measured from 1 January as day 1.
   (iv) Write down the angular frequency ω of this variation.
   (v) Derive an expression for the time of sunrise in minutes after midnight in terms of the day, D, of the year.
   (vi) Use the result in part (v) to find the time of sunrise in hours and minutes (am) at the end of April (day 120 of the year).
   [MEI]

15 An engineer seeks to model the oscillatory motion of a suspension system as simple harmonic motion. She observes the motion of a point P which moves vertically about a mean position O. The displacement above O is x metres. At time t seconds the displacement of P above O is x metres. When $t = 0$, P is at its highest point.

The engineer records the distance between the highest and lowest points reached by P to be 0.1 m and the time for 20 oscillations to be 6.4 seconds.
   (i) Write down the amplitude and the period of the motion.
   (ii) Calculate the velocity and acceleration of the point P when it is first 0.02 m below O, specifying the direction in each case.
   (iii) Sketch a graph of x against t for the first oscillation.
   (iv) Write down an expression for x in terms of t. Hence, or otherwise, calculate the time at which P first reaches the point 0.02 m below O while travelling upwards.
   [MEI]

Alternative forms of the equation for SHM

In the previous section you saw that $x = a\sin\omega t$ and $x = a\cos\omega t$ are solutions of the SHM differential equation $\ddot{x} = -\omega^2 x$. In this section you look at a number of alternative forms of the solution, in each case showing that they satisfy the SHM differential equation.

The forms $x = a\sin(\omega t + \varepsilon)$ and $x = a\cos(\omega t + \varepsilon)$

Since the graph of $x = a\sin\omega t$ passes through the origin, it represents SHM in which the particle is at the centre of its oscillation at time zero. Similarly, $x = a\cos\omega t$ represents SHM in which the particle is initially at maximum positive displacement. There will be times when you need to write an expression for SHM which starts at some other point in the cycle, and this is done by introducing a phase shift of an angle ε (the Greek letter 'epsilon'). This is equivalent to a phase shift in the time of $\dfrac{\varepsilon}{\omega}$ since $\omega t + \varepsilon = \omega\left(t + \dfrac{\varepsilon}{\omega}\right)$.

The equation $x = a\sin\omega t$ then becomes $x = a\sin(\omega t + \varepsilon)$, and the effect of this on the graph is shown in figure 3.10. The effect on $x = a\cos\omega t$ is similar.

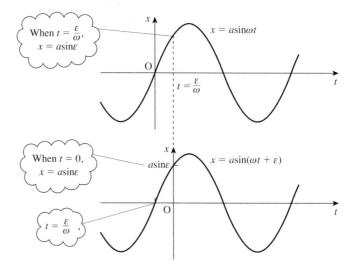

Figure 3.10

EXAMPLE 3.4

The functions f and g are given by

$$f: x = a\sin(\omega t + \varepsilon) \text{ and } g: x = a\cos(\omega t + \varepsilon)$$

where ε (epsilon) is a positive constant.

For each of these functions:

(i) Differentiate it with respect to time to find v (or $\dot{x}$) and show that $v^2 = a^2(\omega^2 - x^2)$.

(ii) Differentiate v with respect to time to find $\ddot{x}$ and show that $\ddot{x} = -\omega^2 x$.

SOLUTION

(i) For f:

$$x = a\sin(\omega t + \varepsilon)$$
$$\Rightarrow \quad v = \dot{x} = a\omega\cos(\omega t + \varepsilon) \tag{1}$$

Therefore
$$v^2 = a^2\omega^2\cos^2(\omega t + \varepsilon)$$
$$= \omega^2[a^2 - a^2\sin^2(\omega t + \varepsilon)]$$
$$\Rightarrow \quad v^2 = \omega^2(a^2 - x^2)$$

Similarly for g:
$$x = a\cos(\omega t + \varepsilon)$$
$$\Rightarrow \quad v = \dot{x} = -a\omega\sin(\omega t + \varepsilon) \qquad \text{②}$$

Therefore
$$v^2 = a^2\omega^2\sin^2(\omega t + \varepsilon)$$
$$= \omega^2[a^2 - a^2\cos^2(\omega t + \varepsilon)]$$
$$\Rightarrow \quad v^2 = \omega^2(a^2 - x^2)$$

(ii) Differentiating equation ① gives

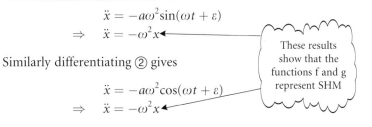

$$\ddot{x} = -a\omega^2\sin(\omega t + \varepsilon)$$
$$\Rightarrow \quad \ddot{x} = -\omega^2 x$$

Similarly differentiating ② gives

$$\ddot{x} = -a\omega^2\cos(\omega t + \varepsilon)$$
$$\Rightarrow \quad \ddot{x} = -\omega^2 x$$

These results show that the functions f and g represent SHM

The form $x = A\sin\omega t + B\cos\omega t$

The function $x = A\sin\omega t + B\cos\omega t$ represents the sum of two SHMs, $A\sin\omega t$ and $B\cos\omega t$. These have the same period $\left(\dfrac{2\pi}{\omega}\right)$ and frequency, but different amplitudes (A and B). They are a quarter of a cycle out of phase because $\sin\omega t = \cos\left(\omega t - \dfrac{\pi}{2}\right) = \cos\omega\left(t - \dfrac{\pi}{2\omega}\right)$.

What is the effect of adding two SHMs in this way?

By differentiating twice with respect to time, you can show that the function obeys the SHM equation $\ddot{x} = -\omega^2 x$.

$$x = A\sin\omega t + B\cos\omega t$$
$$\dot{x} = A\omega\cos\omega t - B\omega\sin\omega t$$
$$\ddot{x} = -A\omega^2\sin\omega t - B\omega^2\cos\omega t$$

This expression for $\ddot{x}$ may be written as

$$\ddot{x} = -\omega^2(A\sin\omega t + B\cos\omega t)$$
and so $\quad \ddot{x} = -\omega^2 x$.

This proves that $x = A\sin\omega t + B\cos\omega t$ represents SHM with period $\dfrac{2\pi}{\omega}$. To show that this form is equivalent to $x = a\sin(\omega t + \varepsilon)$, use the following technique (which you may already have met in *A2 Pure Mathematics*, Chapter 8).

The function $x = A\sin\omega t + B\cos\omega t$ is rewritten as

$$x = \sqrt{A^2 + B^2}\left(\frac{A}{\sqrt{A^2 + B^2}}\sin\omega t + \frac{B}{\sqrt{A^2 + B^2}}\cos\omega t\right)$$

In the right-angled triangle shown in figure 3.11, for the case when A and B are both positive

$$\cos\varepsilon = \frac{A}{\sqrt{A^2 + B^2}} \text{ and } \sin\varepsilon = \frac{B}{\sqrt{A^2 + B^2}}.$$

The hypotenuse is $\sqrt{A^2 + B^2} = a$.

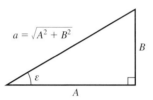

Figure 3.11

Using these results gives

$$x = a(\sin\omega t\cos\varepsilon + \cos\omega t\sin\varepsilon).$$

Using the compound angle formula $\sin(\theta + \phi) = \sin\theta\cos\phi + \cos\theta\sin\phi$, this can be written

$$x = a\sin(\omega t + \varepsilon).$$

Thus the SHM $x = A\sin\omega t + B\cos\omega t$ is equivalent to the SHM $x = a\sin(\omega t + \varepsilon)$, where the amplitude a is $\sqrt{A^2 + B^2}$, and the phase angle ε is given by

$$\sin\varepsilon = \frac{B}{\sqrt{A^2 + B^2}} \text{ and } \cos\varepsilon = \frac{A}{\sqrt{A^2 + B^2}}.$$

This is also equivalent to a cosine form, since for any angle α

$$\sin\alpha = \cos\left(\alpha - \frac{\pi}{2}\right)$$

and so x can be written as

$$x = a\cos\left(\omega t + \varepsilon - \frac{\pi}{2}\right)$$

$$= a\cos(\omega t + \varepsilon') \text{ where } \varepsilon' = \varepsilon - \frac{\pi}{2}.$$

(If ε is an acute angle, ε' is negative.)

The effect of adding together two SHMs of the same period is to create a single SHM, also with the same period but with greater amplitude. This is shown in figure 3.12 for $x = 3\cos t$ and $x = 4\sin t$.

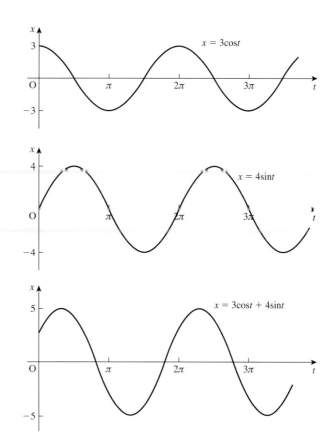

Figure 3.12

❓ When you hear several musical instruments play notes of the same pitch, the vibrations which reach your ears are a combination of oscillations of different amplitudes. In addition, these may have been set in motion at different stages in the cycle and so be out of phase.

How is it possible for the music to sound pleasant?

The form $x = x_0 + a\sin\omega t$

Although the equation $x = x_0 + a\sin\omega t$ does not satisfy the SHM equation $\ddot{x} = -\omega^2 x$, it does represent SHM about the fixed point x_0 as you can see from figure 3.13, overleaf.

You may find it helpful to think of this motion in terms of a new variable, z, representing the displacement from the central position. This is given by

$$z = x - x_0$$
$$= a\sin\omega t.$$

The variable z does satisfy the SHM equation $\ddot{z} = -\omega^2 z$ and all the standard SHM results also hold for z.

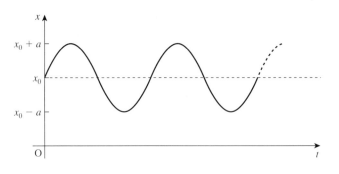

Figure 3.13

Choosing the most appropriate function to model a particular oscillation

You have seen that any particular example of SHM can be described using at least one of a variety of functions.

SHM about $x = 0$ with period $\dfrac{2\pi}{\omega}$, amplitude a	SHM about $x = x_0$ with period $\dfrac{2\pi}{\omega}$, amplitude a
$x = a\sin(\omega t + \varepsilon)$	$x = x_0 + a\sin(\omega t + \varepsilon)$
$x = a\cos(\omega t + \varepsilon)$	$x = x_0 + a\cos(\omega t + \varepsilon)$
$x = A\sin\omega t + B\cos\omega t$	$x = x_0 + A\sin\omega t + B\cos\omega t$
where $\sqrt{A^2 + B^2} = a$	where $\sqrt{A^2 + B^2} = a$

The constants a, A, B and ε are determined by the *initial conditions*, that is the speed, direction and displacement at time zero.

You will find it helpful to sketch the graph of the oscillation. This will show you the initial conditions and help you to choose the most appropriate form.

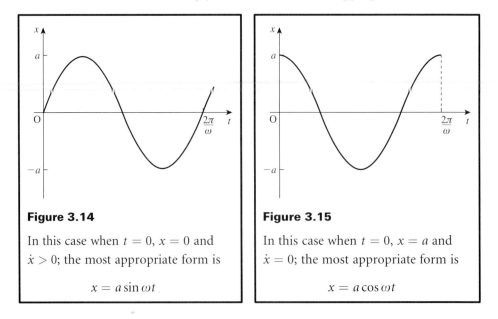

Figure 3.14

In this case when $t = 0$, $x = 0$ and $\dot{x} > 0$; the most appropriate form is

$$x = a\sin\omega t$$

Figure 3.15

In this case when $t = 0$, $x = a$ and $\dot{x} = 0$; the most appropriate form is

$$x = a\cos\omega t$$

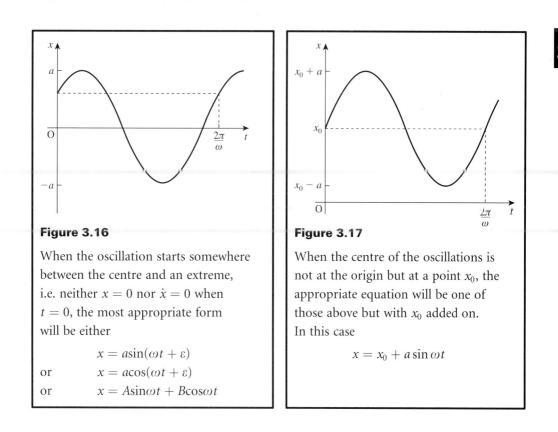

Figure 3.16

When the oscillation starts somewhere between the centre and an extreme, i.e. neither $x = 0$ nor $\dot{x} = 0$ when $t = 0$, the most appropriate form will be either

$$x = a\sin(\omega t + \varepsilon)$$
or $\qquad x = a\cos(\omega t + \varepsilon)$
or $\qquad x = A\sin\omega t + B\cos\omega t$

Figure 3.17

When the centre of the oscillations is not at the origin but at a point x_0, the appropriate equation will be one of those above but with x_0 added on. In this case

$$x = x_0 + a\sin\omega t$$

? The graphs below show cases where the initial conditions are different from those covered above. What are the most appropriate forms to model these oscillations?

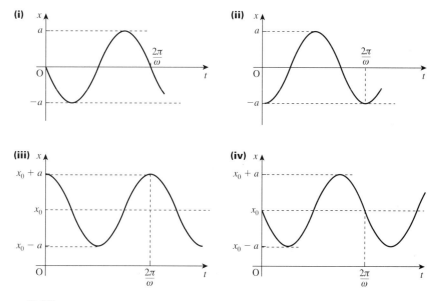

Figure 3.18

EXAMPLE 3.5

A particle is moving with SHM of period π. Initially it is 10 cm from the centre of the motion and moving in the positive direction with a speed of $6\,\text{cm s}^{-1}$. Find an equation to describe the motion.

SOLUTION

The information given is shown in the diagram below.

Figure 3.19

The initial speed is positive, so an appropriate equation is

$$x = a\sin(\omega t + \varepsilon),$$

and you need to find the values of a, ω, and ε.

Finding $\boldsymbol{\omega}$

Since the period of the motion is π,

$$\frac{2\pi}{\omega} = \pi \quad \Rightarrow \quad \omega = 2.$$

Finding a

Using

$$v^2 = \omega^2(a^2 - x^2)$$
$$6^2 = 2^2(a^2 - 10^2)$$
$$\Rightarrow \quad a = \sqrt{109}$$

Finding ε

Substituting $t = 0$ in $x = a\sin(\omega t + \varepsilon)$ gives

$$10 = \sqrt{109}\,\sin\varepsilon$$
$$\Rightarrow \quad \varepsilon = 1.28\,\text{rad (see Note below)}.$$

So the equation for the motion is

$$x = \sqrt{109}\,\sin(2t + 1.28).$$

Note

When finding ε you must be careful that you have selected the correct root of the equation. In this case at $t = 0$ the particle has positive displacement and positive velocity (it is on its way out and not on its way back), so $t = 0$ corresponds to an angle between 0 and $\frac{\pi}{2}$. The next root of the equation $10 = \sqrt{109}\,\sin\varepsilon$ is $(\pi - 1.28)$. This lies between $\frac{\pi}{2}$ and π and would be the correct value if the particle were on its way back, with displacement $+10$ and velocity -6.

SHM as the projection of circular motion

There is a close relationship between circular motion at constant speed and SHM. This can be illustrated by rotating a bob on the end of a string in a horizontal circle with constant angular velocity, thus forming a conical pendulum. If this is done between the light of an overhead projector and the wall, the shadow of the bob on the wall will perform SHM. (For true SHM the rays of light should be parallel and an approximation to this can be achieved if the pendulum is close to the wall and the overhead projector is as far away as possible.)

Assuming the rays of light are parallel, figure 3.20 shows the position, C, of the bob and its shadow, P, at a particular instant. As the bob moves round the circle from A to B, the shadow moves along the straight line from L to N.

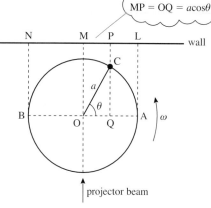

Assuming that $t = 0$ when the bob is at A, the angle θ is given by ωt, where ω is the angular speed of the bob. Thus

$$MP = OQ = a\cos\omega t.$$

Figure 3.20

This is one of the standard forms of SHM.

Note

The projection of uniform circular motion on to a straight line, illustrated here, is the only case where ω actually does represent a physical angular velocity.

EXAMPLE 3.6

An astronomer observes a faint object close to a star. Continued observations show the object apparently moving in a straight line through the star as shown in the diagram

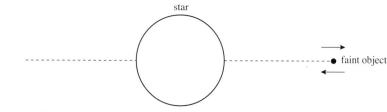

Figure 3.21

The astronomer is able to estimate the apparent distance of the object from the centre of the star and records this at 30-day intervals, resulting in the following table.

Day, t	0	30	60	90	120
Distance (10^{11} m), x	1.0	1.5	1.9	2.0	1.9

The astronomer thinks that the object is a planet moving around the star in a circular orbit and that she is observing it from a point in the plane of the orbit. She decides to model the apparent distance from the centre by the SHM equation:

$$x = 2\sin(\omega t + \varepsilon)$$

(i) Use the values of x for $t = 0$ and $t = 90$ to find values for the constants ω and ε and verify that the other values of x are consistent with this model.

(ii) Assuming the model is correct, find

    (a) the radius of the orbit

    (b) the speed of the planet

    (c) the number of earth days the planet takes to go round its star.

[MEI]

SOLUTION

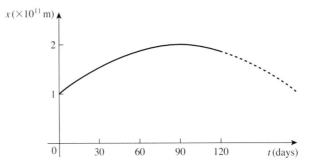

Figure 3.22

(i) Using $x = 2\sin(\omega t + \varepsilon)$:

    When $t = 0$, $x = 1$ so $1 = 2\sin\varepsilon$

                                 $\Rightarrow$ $\varepsilon = \dfrac{\pi}{6}$

The equation $\sin\varepsilon = \frac{1}{2}$ has other roots $\left(\text{e.g.} \dfrac{5\pi}{6}\right)$, but the graph shows that $\dfrac{\pi}{6}$ is the one you want.

When $t = 90$, $x = 2$ so $2 = 2\sin\left(90\omega + \dfrac{\pi}{6}\right)$

$$\Rightarrow \quad \sin\left(90\omega + \frac{\pi}{6}\right) = 1$$

$$\Rightarrow \quad 90\omega + \frac{\pi}{6} = \frac{\pi}{2}$$

$$\Rightarrow \quad \omega = \frac{\pi}{270}$$

So the model is $\qquad\qquad\qquad\qquad x = 2\sin\left(\dfrac{\pi t}{270} + \dfrac{\pi}{6}\right)$

For the other values of t:

t	observed displacement	model's prediction
30	1.5	$2\sin\left(\dfrac{\pi}{9} + \dfrac{\pi}{6}\right) = 1.53$
60	1.9	$2\sin\left(\dfrac{2\pi}{9} + \dfrac{\pi}{6}\right) = 1.88$
120	1.9	$2\sin\left(\dfrac{4\pi}{9} + \dfrac{\pi}{6}\right) = 1.88$

This shows that the model is a very good predictor of the actual position of the object.

(ii) (a) The radius of the orbit is the amplitude a of the motion:

$$\text{radius} = 2 \times 10^{11} \text{ m}$$

(b) The speed of the planet is

$$a\omega = 2 \times 10^{11} \times \frac{\pi}{270} = 2.3 \times 10^{9} \text{ ms}^{-1}$$

(c) The total time for one orbit is the period of the SHM i.e. $\dfrac{2\pi}{\omega}$

$$\text{Number of days} = 2\pi \div \frac{\pi}{270}$$
$$= 540 \text{ days}$$

Historical note

In 1822, the French mathematician Jean Baptiste Fourier (1768–1830) showed that any function of t can be written as a sum of sines of multiples of t and this is now called a Fourier series. It follows that any vibration which can be written as a function of t can be reproduced by adding simple harmonic vibrations. Fourier accompanied Napoleon to Egypt in 1798 and was made a baron ten years later. He discovered this theorem while working on the flow of heat.

1 (i) Sketch graphs of the following functions:
   (a) $x = 3\cos t$
   (b) $x = 3\cos 2t$
   (c) $x = 3\cos t + 4\sin t$
   (d) $x = 5\cos(0.2t + \dfrac{\pi}{4})$

(ii) In each case write down the amplitude, period and frequency of the oscillations.

2 Find a suitable simple harmonic model giving x (in m) in terms of t (in s) for each of the following.
   (i) Period $= 3$ s, and initially $\dot{x} = 0$ and $x = 5$.
   (ii) Period $= 2$ s, amplitude $= 6$ m, and initially $x = 0$.
   (iii) Period $= 5$ s, amplitude $= 4$ m, and initially $x = 2$.
   (iv) Period $= 4$ s, and initially $x = 1.5$ and $\dot{x} = 6$.

3 The displacement of a particle along a straight line at time t is given by

$$x = 4\cos\left(\frac{\pi t}{12} + \frac{\pi}{6}\right)$$

   (i) Sketch the displacement–time curve.
   (ii) Is it possible to describe x by the equation

$$x = p\sin\omega t + q\cos\omega t?$$

   If so, find the values of p and q.

4 The displacements of a particle along a straight line at different times are given in the table below.

t	0	1	2	3	4	5	6	7	8	9
x	3.54	5	3.54	0	-3.54	-5	-3.54	0	3.54	5

   (i) These data may be modelled using the SHM equation

$$x = a\cos(\omega t - \varepsilon).$$

   Find the values of a, ω and ε.
   (ii) An alternative equation is $x = a\sin(\omega t + \delta)$
   Find the value of δ.
   (iii) A third equation to describe the data is

$$x = b\sin\omega t + b\cos\omega t$$

   Find the value of b and show that this form of the equation does indeed describe the data.

5 A particle is executing SHM. Its position, y (in m), at time t (in s) is given in the table below.

t	2	4	6	8	10	12	14	16
y	8	5.4	5.4	8	10.6	10.6	8	5.4

(i) Draw the graph of y against t and write down the central value of y for the motion.

The motion may be described by the equation

$$y = y_0 + a\cos(\omega t + \varepsilon)$$

(ii) Use the information in the table to determine the values of ω, ε and a.

6 A SHM is described by the equation

$$x = 2\cos\frac{\pi}{4}t + \sqrt{5}\sin\frac{\pi}{4}t$$

(i) Plot the graph of x against t for $0 \leqslant t \leqslant 20$.

The motion may be described by an equation of the form

$$x = a\sin(\omega_1 t + \varepsilon)$$

(ii) Determine the values of a, ω_1 and ε.

Another way of describing the motion is given by the equation

$$x = b\cos(\omega_2 t + \delta)$$

(iii) State which of b, ω_2 and δ are equal, respectively, to a, ω_1 and ε.
(iv) State the values of b, ω_2 and δ.

7 As a result of storms in different places, two swell wave patterns, both running in the same direction, occur at the same time over a stretch of open sea. Their heights above the mean sea level can be modelled as follows.

Wave pattern A: $h_A = 1.5\sin\frac{\pi}{15}t$ (t is in s, h is in m)

Wave pattern B: $h_B = 2\cos\frac{\pi}{15}t$

(i) Plot the two wave patterns on the same piece of graph paper taking values of t from 0 to 45 at 5-s intervals.
(ii) The overall height of the water, h, is given by

$$h = h_A + h_B$$

Plot the values of h for $0 \leqslant t \leqslant 45$ on the same graph that you used for h_A and h_B.

(iii) Show algebraically that the effect of the two wave patterns is that of a single wave pattern described by

$$h = a\sin(\omega t + \varepsilon)$$

and state the values of a, ω and ε.

8 The centre of the London Eye observation wheel is approximately 70 m above the ground (about as high as Big Ben which is on the opposite side of the Thames). The wheel's diameter is 135 m and it takes 30 minutes to make one revolution. Assuming that it turns continuously at a steady speed, find the angular velocity of the wheel.

(i) Write down a suitable equation for the height above the ground of a passenger t minutes after boarding at the lowest level.

(ii) Estimate for how long during a flight of one revolution passengers are higher than the highest point on the Houses of Parliament (102 m).

9 A piston performs simple harmonic motion with amplitude 0.1 m about a point O. The displacement from O is denoted by x metres and the time by t seconds. In a test, the piston is first observed at $t = 0$ when $x = 0.05$ and it is moving *towards* O.

(i) Sketch a graph of x against t for one complete oscillation starting at $t = 0$.

An expression for x of the form $x = a\sin(\omega t + \varepsilon)$ is sought, where a, ω and ε are positive constants.

(ii) Write down the value of a and find the value of ε.

The piston passes through O after 0.025 seconds.

(iii) Calculate ω and the period of the motion.

(iv) Calculate the acceleration of the piston when it is first observed.

[MEI]

10 The positions of the points B, B′, A, A′ and O are shown on the diagram below.

B′   A′   O   A   B   → x
$-b$ $-a$ a b

A particle is released from rest at the point B at time $t = 0$ and moves in a simple harmonic motion, centre O, with period $\dfrac{2\pi}{\omega}$.

(i) Write down an expression for the displacement x from O of the particle at time t.

(ii) Write down an expression for the speed v of the particle as it passes the point A and show that $b = \sqrt{a^2 + \dfrac{v^2}{\omega^2}}$.

(iii) Show that the time taken by the particle to travel directly from A to A′ is given by $\dfrac{1}{\omega}\left[\pi - 2\arccos\left(\dfrac{a}{b}\right)\right]$.

A second particle is released from rest at the point A at time $t = 0$. It moves in a simple harmonic motion, centre O, with period $\dfrac{2\pi}{\omega}$.

(iv) How much longer does this particle take to travel from A to A′?

A machine component is subject to a variable force which causes it to move with simple harmonic motion. When released from rest at point A it travels 0.4 m before coming momentarily to rest after 0.1 s. It is desired to shorten the time of the motion of the component over the 0.4 m and this is to be achieved by giving the component an initial speed of 2 ms^{-1}.

(v) Assuming that the same law of force applies to the new motion, calculate the time saved.
[Hint: Use the result obtained in part (ii) to find the amplitude of the simple harmonic motion the component would have if it were released from rest and passed through point A at 2 ms^{-1}.]

[MEI]

11 Data on sunspots show that their number in any year, N, follows an 11-year cycle. An approximate model gives N as $N = N_0 + a\cos\omega T$ where T is the number of years (0, 1, 2, 3, ...) since the year in which there was last a maximum. A maximum of 150 occurred in 1948 and the subsequent minimum was 20.

(i) Determine the appropriate values of N_0, a and ω from the given information.

(ii) Estimate the numbers of sunspots in 1950 and 1955.

12 The height, h m, of water above the bottom of a harbour varies with the tide.

The vertical motion of a piece of wood floating on the surface may be modelled by the equation

$$h = h_0 + a\sin(\omega t + \varepsilon)$$

where t is the time in hours since midnight.

(i) Describe the vertical motion of the piece of wood in terms of h_0, a and ω.

The heights at certain times on one day are given by:

t **(hours)**	2	5	8	11	12
h **(metres)**	10	6	2	6	8

(ii) Find the values of h_0, a, ω and ε.

(iii) What are the vertical speed and acceleration of the piece of wood when $t = 8.6$?

(iv) What is the greatest speed at which the water level rises?

13 The motion of the fore and hind wings of a locust can be modelled approximately using the ideas of oscillation. The motion of the fore wings is modelled by

$$\alpha = 1.5 + 0.5\sin(1.05t - 0.005)$$

where α is the angle between the fore wing and the vertical, and t is measured in hundredths of a second.

(i) Find the period and the amplitude of the motion.

The hind wings initially make an angle of 1.5 rad to the vertical, then they oscillate with period 0.06 s and amplitude 1.5 rad.

(ii) Construct a model of the form

$$\beta = \beta_0 + a\sin(kt)$$

for the motion of the hind wings.

Oscillating mechanical systems

There are very many mechanical systems which can be modelled using SHM. Two of these are the spring–mass oscillator and the simple pendulum. The motion of the simple pendulum approximates to SHM for small angles as you will see in the next section.

The simple pendulum

A simple pendulum consists of a bob suspended on the end of a light inelastic string as illustrated by the apparatus in figure 3.23.

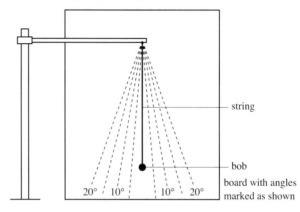

Figure 3.23

EXPERIMENT

Set up the apparatus as shown, making sure that the board is as close as possible to the pendulum without touching it. Use the apparatus to investigate whether the period of small oscillations depends on

(i) the mass of the bob
(ii) the length of the string
(iii) the amplitude of the swing
(iv) the starting point in the cycle.

In order to construct a mathematical model for the motion of a simple pendulum, consider a general position some time t after it has been set in motion, when the string makes an angle θ with the vertical.

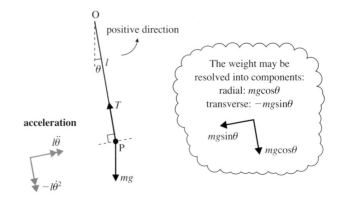

Figure 3.24

The forces acting on the bob are the tension in the string and the force of gravity mg, where m is the mass of the bob as shown in figure 3.24. It swings through a small arc of a circle of radius l where l is the length of the string.

There is no motion in the radial direction. In the transverse direction, the acceleration, $l\ddot{\theta}$, is given by

$$-mg\sin\theta = ml\ddot{\theta}$$

$$\Rightarrow \quad \ddot{\theta} = -\frac{g}{l}\sin\theta$$

When the angle is measured in radians, $\theta \approx \sin\theta$ for small angles (up to about 0.3 rad for accuracy correct to 2 d.p.). In this case:

$$\ddot{\theta} = -\frac{g}{l}\theta$$

This is the standard equation for SHM, $\ddot{x} = -\omega^2 x$, with x replaced by θ and ω^2 replaced by $\frac{g}{l}$.

A pendulum is usually set in motion by pulling the bob to one side, say to an angle α, and then releasing it from rest. If this is the case, $\theta = \alpha$ and $\dot{\theta} = 0$ when $t = 0$.

The appropriate form of the SHM equation is

$$\theta = \alpha\cos\sqrt{\frac{g}{l}}t.$$

$\theta = \alpha$ and $\dot{\theta} = 0$ when $t = 0$

The period is given by

$$T = \frac{2\pi}{\omega} = 2\pi\sqrt{\frac{l}{g}}$$

There are several points to note:

- The SHM involves the angular displacement, θ, rather than the linear displacement of the bob.
- SHM is a good model for small values of θ, but the approximation becomes less good with increasing θ.
- The mass of the bob is not present in the SHM equation, so its value does not affect the motion.
- The amplitude is specified only by the initial conditions.
- The period $2\pi\sqrt{\dfrac{l}{g}}$ is not affected by the amplitude of the motion or the mass

  of the bob. It depends only on g and the length of the string.
- It is important not to confuse the angular velocity, $\dot{\theta}$, of the pendulum with ω, the angular frequency of the SHM.

 Use a calculator to find positive values of θ which differ from $\sin\theta$ by less than

(i) 0.05%   (ii) 1%   (iii) 2%.

EXAMPLE 3.7

A simple pendulum consists of a mass hanging on the end of a light inextensible string. The angle θ radians between the string and the vertical satisfies the

differential equation $\ddot{\theta} = -\dfrac{g}{l}\theta$.

(i)   Find the length of the pendulum for which the period for small oscillations is 2 s.

The pendulum is released when the string makes an angle of 0.2 rad with the vertical.

(ii) Find an equation for θ in terms of t.
(iii) Find the times when the pendulum is in the equilibrium position.
(iv) Find also the time taken for the pendulum to move from the equilibrium position to a point half-way to the end of the oscillation.

SOLUTION

(i)   The equation of motion, $\ddot{\theta} = -\dfrac{g}{l}\theta$, is the SHM differential equation with

$\omega^2 = \dfrac{g}{l}$. All the standard results for SHM apply.

The period is 2 s, so $\qquad \dfrac{2\pi}{\omega} = 2 \quad \Rightarrow \quad \omega = \pi.$

Therefore
$$\pi^2 = \frac{g}{l}$$

$$\Rightarrow \qquad l = \frac{g}{\pi^2} = \frac{9.8}{(3.14\dots)^2}$$

The length of the pendulum is 0.993 m or about 1 m.

(ii) The pendulum is released when $\theta = 0.2$ ($\theta = 0.2$ when $t = 0$). The most appropriate function to use to model the motion is

$$\theta = 0.2\cos\omega t$$

You have already seen that $\omega = \pi$

Therefore $\qquad \theta = 0.2\cos\pi t$

(iii) The pendulum is in the equilibrium position when $\theta = 0$, i.e. when

$$0.2\cos\pi t = 0$$

$$\Rightarrow \qquad \cos\pi t = 0$$

$$\Rightarrow \qquad \pi t = \frac{\pi}{2}, \frac{3\pi}{2}, \frac{5\pi}{2} \dots$$

$$\Rightarrow \qquad t = \tfrac{1}{2}, \tfrac{3}{2}, \tfrac{5}{2}, \dots$$

(iv) The pendulum is first at the equilibrium position, $\theta = 0$, when $t = 0.5$.

It is half-way to the end of the oscillation when $\theta = -0.1$.
The value of t when $\theta = -0.1$ is given by

$$0.2\cos\pi t = -0.1$$

$$\Rightarrow \qquad \pi t = \frac{2\pi}{3} \qquad \overbrace{\cos\frac{2\pi}{3} = -0.5}$$

$$\Rightarrow \qquad t = \tfrac{2}{3}.$$

The time taken from the centre to the half-way point is $\frac{2}{3} - \frac{1}{2} = \frac{1}{6}$ s.

The graph illustrates the first two swings of the pendulum.

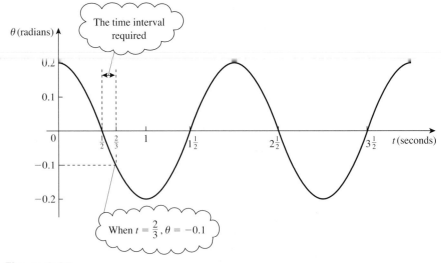

Figure 3.25

Notice that the time taken to travel from the centre half-way to the end is one third of and not half of the time taken to travel to the end. This is because, for SHM, the velocity is greater near the centre of the motion than near the ends.

The spring–mass oscillator

Set up a spring–mass oscillator consisting of a weight suspended by a spring as shown in the diagram.

Use the apparatus to investigate whether the period of small oscillations depends on

(i) the mass of the weight
(ii) the modulus of elasticity of the spring
(iii) the natural length of the spring
(iv) the amplitude of the oscillation.

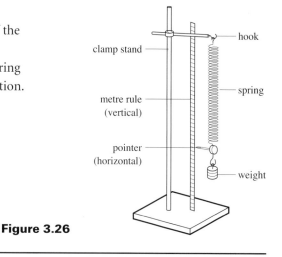

hook
clamp stand
spring
metre rule (vertical)
pointer (horizontal)
weight

Figure 3.26

The equation of motion of a particle suspended from a spring

Figure 3.27 shows a particle of mass m suspended from a perfectly elastic light spring of natural length l_0, and modulus of elasticity λ. The extension of the spring when the particle is hanging in equilibrium is e.

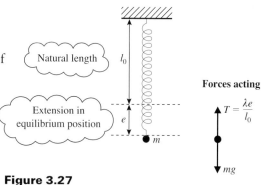

Natural length

l_0

Forces acting

Extension in equilibrium position

e

m

$T = \dfrac{\lambda e}{l_0}$

mg

To find the equation of motion for the particle, start by finding an expression for e.

Figure 3.27

The tension T in the spring is given by $T = \dfrac{\lambda e}{l_0}$ and this is equal to the weight of the particle, mg.

Thus
$$\frac{\lambda e}{l_0} = mg \qquad \qquad ①$$

Now look at the situation when the spring has an extension x in the downwards direction from the equilibrium position as in figure 3.28. The total extension is now $e + x$.

The particle is not in equilibrium, and its acceleration in the downwards direction is denoted by $\ddot{x}$.

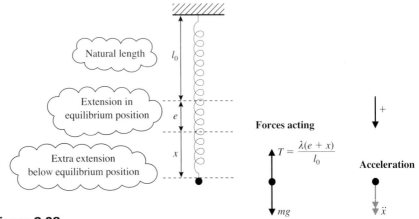

Figure 3.28

There are two forces acting on the particle: the tension in the spring, $T = \dfrac{\lambda(e + x)}{l_0}$, and its weight, mg.

By Newton's second law

$$m\ddot{x} = mg - \frac{\lambda(e + x)}{l_0}$$

$$= mg - \frac{\lambda e}{l_0} - \frac{\lambda x}{l_0}.$$

But from ① $\quad \dfrac{\lambda e}{l_0} = mg$

so $\quad m\ddot{x} = mg - mg - \dfrac{\lambda x}{l_0}.$

Giving the differential equation

$$\ddot{x} = -\frac{\lambda}{ml_0}x$$

This is the standard equation for SHM with

$$\omega^2 = \frac{\lambda}{ml_0}$$

Its period is $\dfrac{2\pi}{\omega} = 2\pi\sqrt{\dfrac{ml_0}{\lambda}}.$

If k is the stiffness of the spring, $k = \dfrac{\lambda}{l_0}$ so this then becomes $2\pi\sqrt{\dfrac{m}{k}}.$

This means that the period of the oscillations depends only on the mass and the stiffness of the spring.

Note that this model is good only so long as Hooke's law holds, but provided this is so, the motion is an example of true SHM, unlike that of the simple pendulum which only approximates to SHM.

EXAMPLE 3.8

A particle of mass 200 g is attached to a light spring of natural length 40 cm and stiffness 50 Nm^{-1}. The particle is allowed to hang vertically in equilibrium.

(i) Find the extension of the spring in this position.

The spring is now pulled down 3 cm and released from rest.

(ii) Find the length of the spring as a function of time.

SOLUTION

(i) The diagram shows the relevant lengths, and the forces acting on the particle in equilibrium. The extension in the spring is x_0 m.

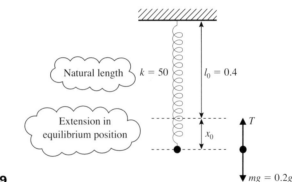

Figure 3.29

By Hooke's law: $\quad T = kx_0 = 50x_0$

Since the particle is in equilibrium,

$$T = 0.2g$$
$$\Rightarrow \quad 50x_0 = 0.2g$$
$$x_0 = 0.0392$$

The extension is 0.0392 m = 3.92 cm.

(ii) Let x m be the displacement from the equilibrium position in the downwards direction.

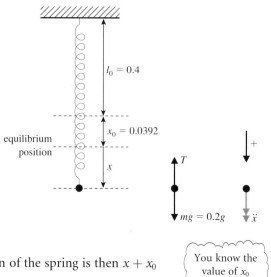

Figure 3.30

The extension of the spring is then $x + x_0$

> You know the value of x_0

By Hooke's law, $\qquad T = 50(x + x_0)$

Applying Newton's second law in the downwards direction,

$$0.2g - 50(x + x_0) = 0.2\ddot{x}$$
$$\Rightarrow \qquad 0.2g - 50x - 50x_0 = 0.2\ddot{x}$$

> This shows the advantage of measuring x from the equilibrium position. The weight and kx_0 cancel each other out

However, as found in part (i), $0.2g = 50x_0$ and so the equation may be simplified to

$$0.2\ddot{x} = -50x$$
$$\Rightarrow \qquad \ddot{x} = -250x.$$

This is the SHM equation with $\omega^2 = 250$, and so $\omega = \sqrt{250}$.

Since the particle starts at the end of the oscillation with $x = 0.03$, the appropriate equation is of the form $x = a\cos\omega t$, with $a = 0.03$ and $\omega = \sqrt{250}$.

So, at time t, $\qquad x = 0.03\cos\sqrt{250}\,t$

and the total length is $0.4 + 0.0392 + 0.03\cos\sqrt{250}\,t$

$$= 0.4392 + 0.03\cos\sqrt{250}\,t$$

❓ Would the period of the oscillations in the above example be the same on the moon?

EXAMPLE 3.9

Two springs have the same modulus of elasticity, 30 N, but are of natural lengths 0.4 m and 0.6 m. An object of mass 0.5 kg is attached to one end of each spring and the other ends are attached to two points which are 1.2 m apart on a smooth horizontal table. Find the period of small oscillations of this system.

SOLUTION

The vertical forces acting on the object, its weight and the normal reaction of the table, have no effect on the motion: they balance each other.

The first step is to find the equilibrium position of the object. The diagram shows the relevant lengths and the horizontal forces acting when the object is in equilibrium. The extensions in the springs are e_1 m and e_2 m and the tension, T N is the same on both sides.

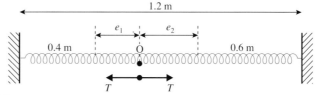

Figure 3.31

Hooke's law applied to each spring gives

$$T = \frac{30}{0.4} \times e_1 = 75e_1$$

and $$T = \frac{30}{0.6} \times e_2 = 50e_2$$

$$\Rightarrow \quad 75e_1 = 50e_2$$
$$\Rightarrow \quad e_2 = 1.5e_1$$

The total length is 1.2 m, so $e_1 + e_2 = 0.2$,
$$\Rightarrow \quad 2.5e_1 = 0.2$$

Hence $$e_1 = 0.08 \text{ and } e_2 = 0.12$$

The next step is to find the equation of motion, so it is necessary to consider a general position for the object, and this is given by the displacement x m from the equilibrium position. The direction towards the right is taken to be positive.

The tensions in the springs are now different.

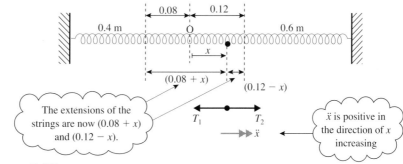

Figure 3.32

Hooke's law gives

$$T_1 = \frac{30}{0.4}(0.08 + x) = 75(0.08 + x)$$

$$T_2 = \frac{30}{0.6}(0.12 - x) = 50(0.12 - x)$$

Newton's second law can now be applied giving

$$T_2 - T_1 = m\ddot{x}$$

$$\Rightarrow \quad 50(0.12 - x) - 75(0.08 + x) = 0.5\ddot{x}$$

$$\Rightarrow \quad -125x = 0.5\ddot{x}$$

$$\Rightarrow \quad \ddot{x} = -250x$$

This is the equation of motion for SHM with $\omega = \sqrt{250}$.

The period is $\dfrac{2\pi}{\omega}$ or $0.40\,\text{s}$ (to 2 d.p.).

In this exercise take g as $9.8\,\text{ms}^{-2}$ (unless otherwise stated).

1 A simple pendulum has length 0.5 m and a bob of mass 0.3 kg.
   (i)   Draw a diagram to show the forces acting on the bob when the string makes an angle of θ rad with the vertical. Show also the radial and transverse components of the acceleration of the bob.
   (ii) Write down the equation of motion of the bob in the transverse direction.
   (iii) State the conditions required for this motion to approximate to SHM.
   (iv) Write down the SHM equation and state the period.
   (v)   Was it necessary to be told the mass of the bob?

2 A simple pendulum of length 3 m has a bob of mass 0.2 kg. It is hanging vertically when it is set in motion by a single, sharp sideways blow to the bob which causes the pendulum to oscillate with an angular amplitude of 5°.
   (i)   State the amplitude in radians.
   (ii) Calculate the approximate period of the pendulum.
   (iii) The motion of the pendulum can be modelled by

   $$\theta = a\sin(\omega t + \varepsilon)$$

   Write down the values of a, ω and ε.
   (iv) Calculate the maximum speed of the pendulum bob according to this model and the impulse of the blow applied to the bob.

3 A pendulum has a bob of mass 0.25 kg. The period of the pendulum is 2 s. The amplitude of its swing is 3°.

(i) Find the length of the pendulum.

(ii) State the effect (if any) on the period of the pendulum of

(a) making the mass of the bob 0.75 kg

(b) doubling the length of the pendulum

(c) halving the amplitude of its swing

(d) moving it to the moon where the acceleration due to gravity is one sixth of that on the earth.

4 A pendulum consists of a stone of mass 0.2 kg attached to a light inelastic string of length 4 m.

(i) Formulate the equation of motion of the stone, stating any assumptions involved.

(ii) Calculate the period of small oscillations.

5 A thin horizontal plate is being driven by a mechanism so that its vertical motion is simple harmonic. It moves through two complete oscillations per second and the distance from the lowest to the highest point of the motion is 0.5 m. At the instant from which time is measured the plate is moving upwards through the centre of its motion. At a time t s later the plate is x m above this central level, as shown in the diagram.

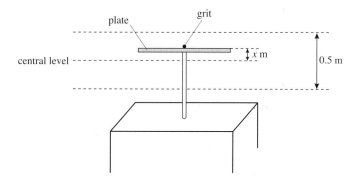

(i) Show that the acceleration, $\ddot{x}$, of the plate is given by

$$\ddot{x} = -16\pi^2 x.$$

(ii) Find an expression for x at time t.

(iii) Find an expression for v^2 in terms of x, where v ms^{-1} is the speed of the plate.

When the plate is at its lowest point, it picks up a small piece of grit of mass m kg.

(iv) Draw a diagram showing the forces acting on the piece of grit while it is in contact with the plate, and derive the equation of motion for the piece of grit. Explain why the grit leaves the plate when $\ddot{x} = -g$.

(v) How far does the piece of grit travel while in contact with the plate? What is its speed when it leaves the plate?

(vi) For how long is the piece of grit in contact with the plate?

[MEI]

6 A loaded test tube of total mass m floats in water and is in equilibrium when a length l is submerged as shown. The upward force exerted by the water on the tube is F.

(i) Why is F equal to mg in the equilibrium position? Given that F is directly proportional to the submerged length, find the constant of proportionality in terms of l, m and g.

The test tube is now pushed down a small amount and released.

(ii) Find F when the bottom of the tube is a distance x below its equilibrium position, and use Newton's second law to write down the equation of motion for the test tube. Show that it will oscillate with SHM with period

$$T = 2\pi \sqrt{\frac{l}{g}}$$

7 A small block of mass 2 kg is attached to a fixed point by a spring of stiffness $10 \, \text{Nm}^{-1}$ and natural length 0.5 m. The block moves in a straight line on a smooth horizontal table. The block is held in a position such that the spring is stretched 0.2 m, and is then released. At time t s later the extension of the spring is x m.

(i) Show that the equation of motion is given by $\ddot{x} + 5x = 0$.

(ii) State the initial conditions for the motion in terms of x and t.

(iii) Show that the expression $x = 0.2\cos\sqrt{5}\,t$ satisfies both parts (i) and (ii).

(iv) State the frequency and amplitude of the block's oscillations.

(v) Find the greatest speed of the block.

8 Two identical springs of natural length 20 cm and stiffness $60 \, \text{Nm}^{-1}$ are attached to a block of mass 200 g and length 5 cm which lies on a smooth table. The other ends of the springs are attached to fixed points 45 cm apart and the springs and the block lie along a straight line as shown in the diagram.

(i) Show that in the equilibrium position there is no tension in either spring.

The block is displaced 2 cm in the negative direction and released. At time t s later, its displacement is x m.

(ii) Write down the equation of motion of the block.

(iii) Write, in terms of x and t, the initial conditions of the motion.

(iv) Write down an expression for the displacement x at any time during the subsequent motion.

(v) State the frequency of the block's oscillations.

(vi) Find the greatest speed and greatest acceleration of the block.

9 A particle, P, of mass m is placed on a smooth, horizontal track and is attached by two springs to fixed points on the track. The spring AP has natural length $3l$ and modulus of elasticity λ. The spring BP has natural length $2l$ and modulus of elasticity 2λ. The points A and B are a distance $6l$ apart.

(i) Find the distance of the equilibrium position from A.
(ii) Find the tensions in the two springs when the particle is in equilibrium.

When the particle is stationary at the equilibrium position, it is given an impulse μ in the direction AB. Its subsequent displacement from the equilibrium position is given by x at time t.

(iii) Write down the equation of motion of the particle and its initial conditions.
(iv) Write down expressions for the amplitude and frequency of the subsequent oscillations.
(v) Find an expression for x in terms of t.

10 A block of mass 750 g hangs vertically, attached to a light elastic string of natural length 50 cm and modulus of elasticity 150 N. The other end of the string is attached to a ceiling.

(i) Taking g to be $10 \, \text{ms}^{-2}$, find the extension of the string in the equilibrium position.

The block is then pulled down a further distance.

(ii) What is the tension in the string when the block is x m below the equilibrium position?
(iii) Show that when the block is allowed to move, its motion is governed by the equation $\ddot{x} = -400x$.

The block is released from a position 2 cm below the equilibrium position.

(iv) Find an expression for the displacement x cm, t s after the block's release.
(v) On another occasion the block is pulled down 3 cm below the equilibrium position. Explain why in this case the subsequent motion is not simple harmonic.

11 Zeb, who should be modelled as a particle of mass m kg, sits on a bouncy toy which behaves like a vertical elastic spring of stiffness $k \, \mathrm{Nm^{-1}}$.

   (i) The spring is compressed a length x_0 m when Zeb sits still in the equilibrium position, E. Show that

$$kx_0 = mg$$

Zeb sets the toy moving so that it performs simple harmonic oscillations.

   (ii) Draw diagrams similar to those on page 120 showing relevant lengths, forces and Zeb's acceleration when he is x m below E. Include the natural length, l, of the spring. Write down Zeb's equation of motion.

  (iii) Obtain the equation for the simple harmonic motion.

  (iv) What is the maximum amplitude if Zeb stays fully in contact with the toy?

12 A block of mass m is to be supported by two elastic strings of natural length l_0 and modulus of elasticity λ.

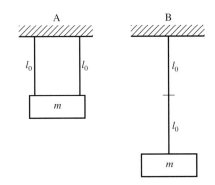

For each of the configurations A and B, find

   (i) the equilibrium position

   (ii) the equation of motion when the block is displaced from the equilibrium position

  (iii) the period of oscillations, assumed small enough for the motion to be simple harmonic, when the block is displaced.

13 A particle of mass 0.02 kg is performing SHM with centre O, period 6 s and amplitude 2 m.

   (i) Find, correct to 2 significant figures in each case,

      (a) the maximum speed V of the particle

      (b) the distance of the particle from O when its speed is $0.9V$

      (c) the magnitude of the force acting on the particle when it is 1 m from O.

   (ii) Show also that the power exerted by the force on the particle is a periodic function of time and state the period.

14 One end of a light, perfectly elastic string of natural length 4 m is suspended from a point O. A small object of mass 10 kg attached to the other end of the string hangs in equilibrium at a point E which is 5 m vertically below O.

   (i) Calculate the stiffness of the string.

The object is dropped from a point D in the line OE and first comes momentarily to rest when it is 2 m below E. Air resistance may be neglected.

   (ii) Show that, while the string is taut, the motion of the object corresponds to simple harmonic motion about E. Express the simple harmonic motion in the form $x = A\cos\omega t$, where x is the displacement of the object below E and t is the time in seconds after the object reaches its lowest point.

When the object rises from its lowest point its motion initially corresponds to simple harmonic motion and when the string becomes slack it moves freely under gravity.

   (iii) What period of time elapses between the object being at the lowest point of the motion and the string becoming slack?

   (iv) What is the speed of the object when the string first becomes slack?

   (v) What period of time elapses between the object being at the lowest point of its motion in two consecutive oscillations?

[MEI]

15 A weighing machine is being designed. It consists of a square platform of mass 2.5 kg supported by a number of identical springs each of stiffness $25\,000\,\mathrm{Nm}^{-1}$, which are attached to a fixed horizontal base as shown in the diagram.

Throughout this question assume that the platform remains horizontal.

Initially the designer uses four springs and the system is in equilibrium.

   (i) Calculate the compression in each spring before any object is placed on the platform.

A child of mass 30 kg is standing on the platform, which is at rest.

   (ii) Calculate the compression in each of the four springs.

   (iii) Calculate the minimum number of additional springs required to reduce the compression to less than 0.002 m.

The 30 kg child is standing on the platform supported by four springs as in the original design. The child's father lifts her off quickly, allowing the platform to oscillate freely in a vertical direction.

(iv) The displacement of the platform *below* the equilibrium position at time t seconds is y metres. Write down the equation of motion for the platform. Hence show that the platform performs simple harmonic motion of period $\frac{1}{100}\pi$ s. Calculate the maximum speed of the platform.

[MEI]

Pendulums

Compare the periods of a simple pendulum and a conical pendulum. What length for a conical pendulum is equal to the length of a simple pendulum with the same period?

Clocks

Before the use of quartz, clocks were regulated by means of pendulums or springs.

1 How long must a simple pendulum be for its period to be
   (i) 1 s   (ii) 2 s?

Explain these lines from a well-known song:

> 'My grandfather's clock was too tall for the shelf,
> so it stood 90 years on the floor . . .
> Tick, tock, tick, tock, his life's seconds numbering.'

Would a 'grandmother' clock, which has a period of 1 s, need to stand on the floor?

2 Investigate the use of clocks in navigation. Why would a standard clock using a pendulum not keep good time on a long voyage?

Historical note

The story of the quest for a means to measure longitude shows why scientists at the time of Hooke were interested in both astronomy and accurate time keeping. The problem was solved by John Harrison whose increasingly accurate clocks are preserved at the old Greenwich Observatory. You can find out more about Hooke and Harrison at the website of the National Maritime Museum: *www.nmm.ac.uk.*

1 Motion for which $\ddot{x} = -\omega^2 x$ is simple harmonic.

2 The graph illustrates the amplitude and period of simple harmonic motion.

3 The speed at displacement x is given by $v^2 = \omega^2(a^2 - x^2)$

4 The period is

$$T = \frac{2\pi}{\omega}$$

5 The frequency is

$$f = \frac{1}{T} = \frac{\omega}{2\pi}$$

6 Different ways of expressing SHM

Initial conditions	Displacement x	Velocity $v = \dot{x}$	Acceleration $\ddot{x}$
$x = 0$ and $\dot{x} > 0$	$a\sin\omega t$	$a\omega\cos\omega t$	$-a\omega^2\sin\omega t$
$x = a$ and $\dot{x} = 0$	$a\cos\omega t$	$-a\omega\sin\omega t$	$-a\omega^2\cos\omega t$
Otherwise (i)	$a\cos(\omega t + \varepsilon)$	$-a\omega\sin(\omega t + \varepsilon)$	$-a\omega^2\cos(\omega t + \varepsilon)$
or (ii)	$a\sin(\omega t + \varepsilon)$	$a\omega\cos(\omega t + \varepsilon)$	$-a\omega^2\sin(\omega t + \varepsilon)$
or (iii)	$A\cos\omega t + B\sin\omega t$	$-A\omega\sin\omega t + B\omega\cos\omega t$	$-\omega^2(A\cos\omega t + B\sin\omega t)$

where $a = \sqrt{A^2 + B^2}$

For all these functions $x = 0$ in the position of equilibrium. If x takes another value, x_0, in the equilibrium position, then $\ddot{x} = -\omega^2(x - x_0)$ and x_0 must be added to functions in the displacement column.

7 For mechanical systems oscillating with simple harmonic motion, $\ddot{x} = -\omega^2 x$,

- the centre of motion is always a position of equilibrium
- for a spring–mass oscillator, x is *not* the extension of the spring
- for a simple pendulum x is the angular displacement, θ, which is small
- ω is *not* the angular velocity of a simple pendulum.

4 Volumes of revolution and centres of mass by integration

Here's fine revolution, an we had the trick to see't.

Hamlet, *William Shakespeare*

What do the shapes of the objects have in common? For each one, suggest a way of finding its volume.

How would you find the volume of
(i) an egg?
(ii) a table tennis ball?
(iii) the moon?

Calculating volumes

One way of finding the volume of an irregular shape is to immerse it in water and measure the apparent increase in the volume of the water. This method is satisfactory for finding the volume of something small and dense like an egg, but you would find it difficult to use for a table tennis ball, and it would be impossible to find the volume of the moon in this way!

You will be familiar with the formula $V = \frac{4}{3}\pi r^3$ for the volume of a sphere. The methods you meet in this chapter will enable you to prove this formula, and also to calculate the volumes of other solids with *rotational symmetry* like the ones illustrated above.

Volumes of revolution

If a set-square (without a hole) is rotated through $360°$ about one of its shorter sides its face will sweep out a solid cone (figure 4.1(a)). A $60°$ set-square will sweep out different cones depending on the side chosen. In the same way a semi-circular protractor will sweep out a sphere if it is rotated completely about its diameter as shown in figure 4.1(b).

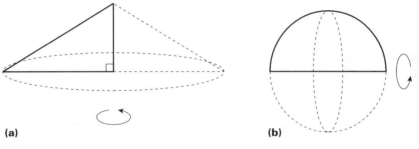

(a)   **(b)**

Figure 4.1

The cone and sphere are examples of *solids of revolution*. If any region of a plane is rotated completely about an axis in the plane it will form a solid of revolution and any solid body with rotational symmetry can be formed in this way.

Imagine that such a solid is cut into thin slices perpendicular to the axis of rotation just as a potato is sliced to make crisps (figure 4.2). Each slice will approximate to a thin disc, but the discs will vary in radius. The volume of the solid can be found by adding the volumes of these discs and then finding the limit of the volume as their thickness approaches zero. When thin discs are used to find a volume they are called *elementary discs*. (Similarly, when thin strips are used to find an area they are called *elementary strips*.)

Thin slices are approximately cylindrical

Figure 4.2

This is essentially the same procedure as that developed for finding the area under a curve (*AS Pure Mathematics*, Chapter 9), and so, as then, integration is required.

Volumes of revolution about the *x* axis

Look at the solid formed by the rotation about the *x* axis of the region under the graph of $y = f(x)$ between the values $x = a$ and $x = b$ as shown in figure 4.3. (You should always start by drawing diagrams when finding areas and volumes.)

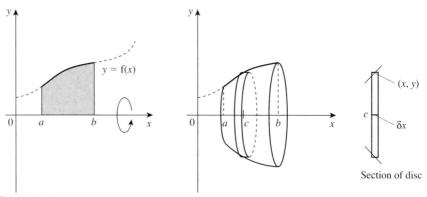

Figure 4.3

The volume of the solid of revolution (which is usually called the volume of revolution) can be found by imagining that it can be sliced into thin discs.

Each disc is a thin cylinder of radius *y* and thickness δx, so its volume is given by

$$\delta V = \pi y^2 \delta x$$

The volume of the solid is the limit of the sum of all these elementary volumes as $\delta x \to 0$ i.e. the limit as $\delta x \to 0$ of

$$\sum_{\text{over all} \atop \text{discs}} \delta V = \sum_{x=a}^{x=b} \pi y^2 \, \delta x$$

> You need to do this because the discs are assumed to be cylinders.

The limiting values of sums such as these are integrals so

$$V = \int_a^b \pi y^2 \, dx$$

The limits are *a* and *b* because *x* takes values from *a* to *b*.

It is essential to realise that this integral is written in terms of d*x* and so it cannot be evaluated unless the function *y* is also written in terms of *x*. For this reason the integral is often written as

$$V = \int_a^b \pi \, [f(x)]^2 \, dx.$$

EXAMPLE 4.1

Find the volume of revolution formed when the region between the curve $y = x^2 + 2$, the x axis and the lines $x = 1$ and $x = 3$ is rotated completely about the x axis.

SOLUTION

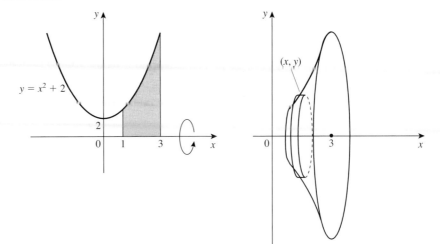

Figure 4.4

The volume is:

$$V = \int_a^b \pi \left[f(x) \right]^2 \, dx$$

$$= \int_1^3 \pi (x^2 + 2)^2 \, dx$$

$$= \int_1^3 \pi (x^4 + 4x^2 + 4) \, dx$$

$$= \left[\pi \left(\frac{x^5}{5} + \frac{4x^3}{3} + 4x \right) \right]_1^3$$

$$= \pi \left[\left(\frac{3^5}{5} + 36 + 12 \right) - \left(\frac{1}{5} + \frac{4}{3} + 4 \right) \right]$$

The volume is $\dfrac{1366\pi}{15}$ cubic units or 286 cubic units correct to 3 significant figures.

Note

Unless a decimal answer is required, it is usual to leave π in the answer, which is then exact.

EXAMPLE 4.2   Find the volume of a spherical ball of radius 2 cm.

SOLUTION

The sphere is formed by rotating the circle $x^2 + y^2 = 4$ about the x axis.

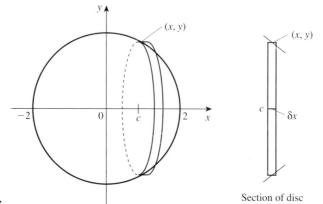

Figure 4.5

The volume of the sphere is found by using

$$V = \int_a^b \pi y^2 \, dx$$

with limits $a = -2$ and $b = 2$.

Since $x^2 + y^2 = 4$, then $y^2 = 4 - x^2$, and the integral may be written as

$$V = \int_{-2}^2 \pi (4 - x^2) \, dx.$$

The constant π can be taken outside the integral so you have

$$V = \pi \left[4x - \frac{x^3}{3} \right]_{-2}^2$$

$$= \pi \left[\left(8 - \frac{8}{3} \right) - \left(-8 + \frac{8}{3} \right) \right]$$

$$= \frac{32\pi}{3} = 33.51 \ldots$$

So the volume of a spherical ball with radius 2 cm is 33.5 cm³ correct to 3 significant figures.

The volume of a sphere

The formula for the volume of a sphere of radius r can be found by following the same argument, but using a circle of radius r rather than one of radius 2 cm. Its equation is $x^2 + y^2 = r^2$ and the limits are $-r$ and r.

$$V = \int \pi y^2 \, dx$$

$$= \int_{-r}^r \pi (r^2 - x^2) \, dx$$

Therefore
$$V = \pi \left[r^2 x - \frac{x^3}{3} \right]_{-r}^{r}$$

$$= \pi \left[\left(r^3 - \frac{r^3}{3} \right) - \left(-r^3 - \frac{-r^3}{3} \right) \right]$$

$$\Rightarrow \quad V = \frac{4}{3} \pi r^3$$

Volumes of revolution about the *y* axis

If the same portion of the curve $y = x^2 + 2$ were to be used to form a region which could be rotated about the *y* axis, a very different solid would be obtained from that on page 135. The region required would be that which lies between the curve and the *y* axis and the limits $y = 3$ and $y = 11$ shown in figure 4.6.

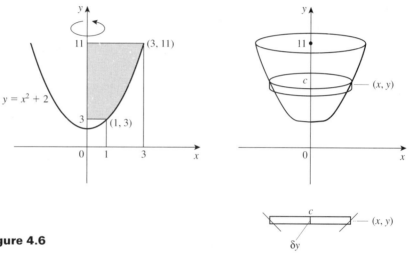

Figure 4.6

An elementary disc has an approximate volume $\delta V = \pi x^2 \delta y$ and the volume of revolution about the *y* axis is given by

$$V = \int \pi x^2 \, dy$$

This time it is necessary to write x^2 in terms of *y*. In this case $x^2 = y - 2$ and so the final integral becomes

$$V = \int_{3}^{11} \pi (y - 2) \, dy$$

$$V = \left[\pi \left(\frac{y^2}{2} - 2y \right) \right]_{3}^{11}$$

$$\Rightarrow \quad V = \pi \left[\left(\frac{11^2}{2} - 22 \right) - \left(\frac{3^2}{2} - 6 \right) \right]$$

The volume is 40π cubic units.

Finding a mathematical model for a solid of revolution

Use an immersion method to find the volumes of two eggs of different shapes or sizes. Measure their lengths and widths as shown in the diagram.

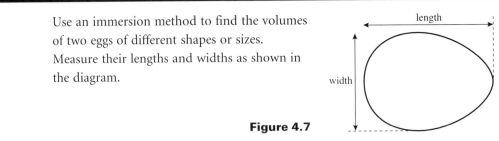

Figure 4.7

We are now going to construct a mathematical model to find the volume of an egg and you will be able to use your measurements to check the accuracy of this model.

A hen's egg has rotational symmetry about its longest axis so it can be represented by a solid of revolution. But what curve should be revolved around the x axis to obtain a reasonable egg shape?

The cross-section looks circular at the 'blunt' end, but the 'sharp' end is longer and looks more like half an ellipse. It may be possible to model the egg as part of a circle plus part of an ellipse, rotated about the x axis. The equation of an ellipse of length $2a$ and width $2b$ as in figure 4.8 can be written as

$$\frac{x^2}{a^2} + \frac{y^2}{b^2} = 1$$

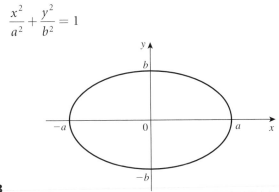

Figure 4.8

A particular egg is 6.3 cm long and 4.6 cm wide. Figure 4.9 shows the regions which are rotated about the x axis.

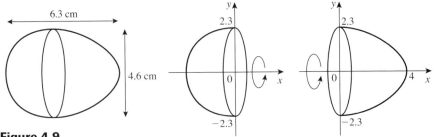

Figure 4.9

The left part is a hemisphere of radius 2.3 cm so its volume is

$$V_1 = \tfrac{2}{3}\pi r^3 = \tfrac{2}{3}\pi(2.3)^3$$
$$= 25.48 \text{ cm}^3 \text{ (to 2 d.p.)}.$$

The equation of the elliptical part to the right is

$$\frac{x^2}{4^2} + \frac{y^2}{2.3^2} = 1$$

On rearrangement this becomes

$$y^2 = 2.3^2\left(1 - \frac{x^2}{4^2}\right)$$

The volume of the elliptical part is therefore given by

$$V_2 = \int_0^4 \pi y^2 \, dx$$
$$= \pi \times 2.3^2 \int_0^4 \left(1 - \frac{x^2}{4^2}\right) dx$$
$$= \pi \times 2.3^2 \left[x - \frac{x^3}{48}\right]_0^4$$
$$= \pi \times 2.3^2 \left[\left(4 - \frac{4^3}{48}\right) - 0\right]$$
$$= 44.32 \text{ cm}^3 \text{ (to 2 d.p.)}.$$

The total volume of the egg can now be found as

$$V_1 + V_2 = 25.48 + 44.32$$
$$= 70 \text{ cm}^3 \text{ (correct to 2 s.f.)}.$$

ACTIVITY

Use this method to calculate the volume of one of the eggs you measured in the experiment, then use the actual volume (found by immersing the egg in water) to check the model against reality.

EXERCISE 4A

1 In each part of this question a region is defined in terms of the lines which form its boundaries.

(a) Draw a sketch of the region.

(b) Find the volume of the solid obtained by rotating it through 360° about the x axis.

(i) $y = 2x$, the x axis and the lines $x = 1$ and $x = 3$.

(ii) $y = \sqrt{x}$, the x axis and the line $x = 4$.

(iii) $y = 2x + 1$, the x axis and the lines $x = 1$ and $x = 5$.

(iv) $y = \dfrac{1}{x}$, the x axis and the lines $x = 1$ and $x = 3$.

(v) $y = 3e^x$, the x axis, the y axis and the line $x = 1.5$.

(vi) $y = \cos x$ (for $0 \leqslant x \leqslant \dfrac{\pi}{2}$), the x axis and the y axis.

(Hint: $\cos^2 x = \tfrac{1}{2}(1 + \cos 2x)$.)

2 In each part of the question a region is defined in terms of the lines which form its boundaries.

(a) Draw a sketch of the region.

(b) Find the volume of the solid obtained by rotating it through 360° about the y axis.

    (i) $y = x^3$, the y axis and the line $y = 8$.

    (ii) $y = 2x - 1$, the y axis and the line $y = 5$.

    (iii) $x^2 + y^2 = 9$, the y axis and the lines $y = 1$ and $y = 3$.

3 **(i)** Sketch the graph of $x^2 + y^2 = 36$.

    (ii) A hemispherical bowl of internal radius 6 cm is filled with water to a depth of 4 cm. Find the volume of water in litres (1 litre $= 1000\,\text{cm}^3$).

4 A mathematical model for a large garden pot is obtained by rotating through 360° about the y axis the part of the curve $y = 0.0001x^4$ which is between $x = 10$ and $x = 25$, and then adding a flat base. Units are in centimetres.

    (i) Draw a sketch of the curve and shade in the cross-section of the pot, indicating which line will form its base.

    (ii) Garden compost is sold in litres. How many litres will be required to fill the pot to a depth of 35 cm? (Ignore the thickness of the pot.)

5 The triangle OAB shown in the diagram is rotated about the x axis to form a solid cone.

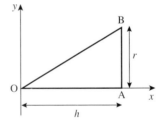

    (i) Find the equation of the line OB.

    (ii) Hence show that the volume of a cone with radius r and height h is $\frac{1}{3}\pi r^2 h$.

6 **(i)** Sketch the ellipse $\dfrac{x^2}{a^2} + \dfrac{y^2}{b^2} = 1$ where $a > b$.

The region under this curve and above the x axis is rotated through 360° about the x axis to form an ellipsoid.

    (ii) Draw a diagram to illustrate the solid formed.

    (iii) Show that the volume of this solid is $\frac{4}{3}\pi b^2 a$.

A mathematical model for an egg is that one end is a half ellipsoid of length a and greatest radius b and the other end is a hemisphere of radius b.

    (iv) Write down the volume of the egg in terms of a and b.

7 (i) Draw a diagram to illustrate the solid formed when the ellipse

$$\frac{x^2}{a^2} + \frac{y^2}{b^2} = 1 \qquad (a > b) \text{ is rotated about the } y \text{ axis.}$$

The photograph shows the elliptical galaxy M87. This galaxy is estimated to have a maximum diameter of 10 000 light years.

(ii) Estimate its volume in metres cubed. (You will need to take measurements from the photograph. The speed of light is approximately $3 \times 10^8 \text{ ms}^{-1}$.)

8 The diagram shows the hyperbola $\dfrac{x^2}{a^2} - \dfrac{y^2}{b^2} = 1$.

When it is rotated through $360°$ about the y axis a hyperboloid is formed.

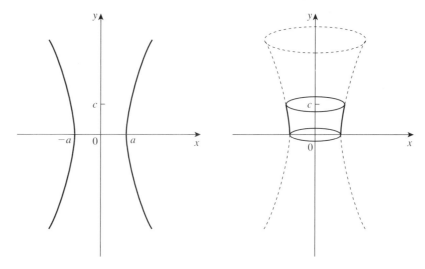

(i) Show that the volume enclosed by this hyperboloid between $y = 0$ and $y = c$ is given by $V = \dfrac{\pi a^2 c}{3b^2}(3b^2 + c^2)$.

The cooling towers of power stations can be modelled as hyperboloids and the dimensions of one such tower, at Didcot power station in Oxfordshire, are shown on the picture.

A = 51.3 m

B = 47.5 m

C = 24.5 m

D = 89.5 m

E = 85.5 m

(ii) Verify that the equation $\dfrac{x^2}{560} - \dfrac{y^2}{3600} = 1$ is a suitable mathematical model for the curve which is rotated to form the hyperboloid.

(iii) Use the formula above to find the volume occupied by the cooling tower, and show that the six towers of the power station occupy over 1.9 million cubic metres of space.

9 A mathematical model for the curved surface of a measuring jug is obtained by rotating the part of the curve $y = 0.003x^4$ between $y = 1$ and $y = 10$ through $360°$ about the y axis. It has a flat base. The units are centimetres.

(i) Sketch the jug.

(ii) Find the values of y for which marks must be placed on the side of the jug to indicate volumes of

    (a) 100 ml   **(b)** 0.5 l   **(c)** 1 l

10 The circle $x^2 + (y + 1)^2 = 5$ meets the x axis at the points A and B. The minor arc AB is rotated about the x axis to form a solid of revolution which can be used to model a rugby ball.

(i) Find the co-ordinates of A and B and show that

$$y^2 = 6 - x^2 - 2\sqrt{5 - x^2}$$

(ii) Hence calculate the volume of the solid of revolution.

$$\left(\text{Hint: } \int_0^2 \sqrt{5 - x^2}\, dx = \frac{5}{2} \arcsin \frac{2}{\sqrt{5}} + 1 \right)$$

(iii) A similar rugby ball is 30 cm long. Find its volume.

Ceramics

It is possible to use the trapezium rule to fine an approximation to any definite integral which cannot be solved analytically or for which an algebraic formula is not known.

Above is a photograph of a group of ceramics made by the potter Hans Coper. Given that the height of the front form is 0.5 m, how could you estimate its external volume using measurements taken from the photograph?

Hot air balloon

It has been said that a hot air balloon contains about a ton of air. Can this be true?

The moon

Describe how the volume of the moon could be estimated using only measurements which can be made by a student and Newton's law of gravitation. (The law states that the force of attraction between bodies of mass m_1 and m_2 whose centres of mass are a distance r apart is given by $\dfrac{Gm_1m_2}{r^2}$ where G is a constant.)

You might need to consider the period of the moon's rotation about the earth, the value of g at the earth's surface and the radius of the earth in order to decide how far the moon is from you. Could you find all these? A metre rule and a small button should then enable you to find the diameter of the moon, and therefore its volume.

Centres of mass

The position of the centre of mass of a solid of revolution will affect its stability and the way it will roll. Some toys are designed so that they can never be knocked over. Many birds that live on cliffs lay pointed eggs which roll round in circles so that they do not fall over the cliff edge. The position of the centre of mass is also important in the design of a lot of sporting equipment.

Using integration to find centres of mass

The calculus methods you have been using to determine the volumes of solids of revolution can be extended to find their centres of mass (assuming they are of uniform density).

Notice that by symmetry, the centre of mass of a solid of revolution must lie on its axis, so provided you choose either the x axis or the y axis to be the axis of symmetry, there is only one co-ordinate to determine. For a solid of revolution about the x axis, divide it into thin discs as before. An elementary disc situated at the point (x, y) on the curve, has a centre of mass at the point $(x, 0)$ on the x axis as shown in figure 4.10.

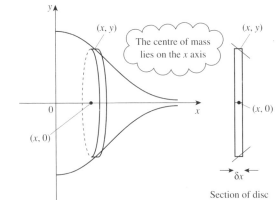

Figure 4.10

The volume of this disc is $\qquad \delta V = \pi y^2 \, \delta x$

and so its mass is $\qquad \delta M = \rho \pi y^2 \, \delta x$

where ρ is the density.

The sum of such discs form a solid which approaches the original as $\delta x \to 0$ and the discs become thinner. Both the mass and the position of the centre of mass are known for each disc, so you can use the result from *Mechanics 2*, Chapter 4. For a composite body, the position, $\bar{x}$, of the centre of mass is given by

Moment of whole mass at centre of mass = Sum of moments of individual masses

$$M\bar{x} = \sum_i m_i x_i$$

In this case:

$$\left(\sum_{\substack{\text{All} \\ \text{discs}}} \delta M \right) \bar{x} = \sum_{\substack{\text{All} \\ \text{discs}}} (\delta M x)$$

Substituting the expression for δM obtained above gives

$$\left(\sum \rho \pi y^2 \, \delta x \right) \bar{x} = \sum \rho \pi y^2 x \, \delta x$$

In the limit as $\delta x \to 0$ these sums may be represented by integrals and so

$$(\textstyle\int \rho \pi y^2 \, \mathrm{d}x) \bar{x} = \int \rho \pi y^2 x \, \mathrm{d}x$$

Assuming that ρ is uniform, you can divide through by $\rho \pi$ to give

$$(\textstyle\int y^2 \, \mathrm{d}x) \bar{x} = \int y^2 x \, \mathrm{d}x \quad \text{or} \quad \bar{x} = \frac{\int y^2 x \, \mathrm{d}x}{\int y^2 \, \mathrm{d}x}$$

This result is valid for any solid of revolution of *uniform density* which is formed by rotation about the x axis.

It may also be written as

$$V\bar{x} = \int \pi y^2 x \, \mathrm{d}x$$

where V is the volume of the solid.

In the next example, the centre of mass of a solid hemisphere is found using the above result.

EXAMPLE 4.3

Find the centre of mass of a solid hemisphere of radius r.

SOLUTION

With the hemisphere oriented as in the diagram, the point (x, y) lies on the curve $x^2 + y^2 = r^2$ and the limits for the integration are $x = 0$ and $x = r$. You also know that the volume, V, is $\frac{2}{3}\pi r^3$ but the equations will look simpler if this is substituted later.

$$V\bar{x} = \int_0^r \pi y^2 x \, \mathrm{d}x$$

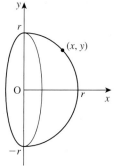

Figure 4.11

Substituting $y^2 = r^2 - x^2$ gives

$$V\bar{x} = \int_0^r \pi(r^2 - x^2)x\,dx$$

$$= \int_0^r \pi(r^2 x - x^3)\,dx$$

$$= \pi\left[\frac{r^2 x^2}{2} - \frac{x^4}{4}\right]_0^r$$

So

$$V\bar{x} = \tfrac{1}{4}\pi r^4$$

Substituting for V gives:

$$\tfrac{2}{3}\pi r^3 \bar{x} = \tfrac{1}{4}\pi r^4$$

$$\Rightarrow \quad \bar{x} = \tfrac{3}{8}r$$

The centre of mass of a solid hemisphere is $\tfrac{3}{8}r$ from the centre of its base.

When finding centres of mass in this way it is often necessary to use *integration by parts* (see *A2 Pure Mathematics*, Chapter 5). The following example illustrates this.

EXAMPLE 4.4

Find the position of the centre of mass of the solid of revolution formed when the region between the curve $y = 2e^x$, the lines $x = 0$ and $x = 2$, and the x axis is rotated through $360°$ about the x axis.

SOLUTION

The diagrams show the region and the solid obtained

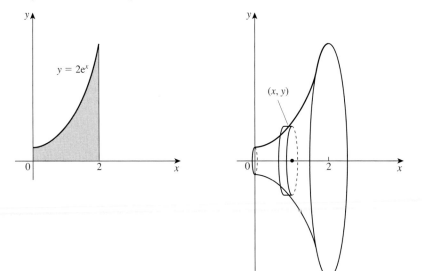

Figure 4.12

The volume, V, of the solid is given by

$$V = \int \pi y^2\,dx$$

$$= \pi \int_0^2 (2e^x)^2\,dx$$

$$V = 4\pi \int_0^2 e^{2x}\, dx$$

$$= 4\pi \left[\frac{e^{2x}}{2} \right]_0^2$$

$$= 2\pi(e^4 - 1).$$

By symmetry, the y co-ordinate of the centre of mass is 0. The x co-ordinate is given by $\bar{x}$ in

$$V\bar{x} = \int \pi y^2 x\, dx$$

$$= \pi \int_0^2 (2e^x)^2 x\, dx$$

Therefore $\qquad V\bar{x} = 4\pi \int_0^2 x e^{2x}\, dx.$ ①

This integral requires the technique of integration by parts, expressed by the general formula

$$\int_a^b u \frac{dv}{dx}\, dx = \left[uv \right]_a^b - \int_a^b v \frac{du}{dx}\, dx.$$

To find $\qquad \int x e^{2x}\, dx$

let $\qquad u = x \quad \Rightarrow \quad \dfrac{du}{dx} = 1,$

and let $\qquad \dfrac{dv}{dx} = e^{2x} \quad \Rightarrow \quad v = \dfrac{e^{2x}}{2}.$

The limits are $a = 0$ and $b = 2$.

Substituting these in the general formula, you obtain

$$\int_0^2 x e^{2x}\, dx = \left[x \frac{e^{2x}}{2} \right]_0^2 - \int_0^2 \frac{e^{2x}}{2} \times 1 \times dx$$

$$= \left[\tfrac{1}{2} x e^{2x} \right]_0^2 - \left[\tfrac{1}{4} e^{2x} \right]_0^2$$

$$= (e^4 - 0) - (\tfrac{1}{4}e^4 - \tfrac{1}{4})$$

$$= \tfrac{1}{4}(3e^4 + 1).$$

Substituting this and $V = 2\pi(e^4 - 1)$ in ①

$$V\bar{x} = 4\pi \int_0^2 x e^{2x}\, dx$$

gives $\qquad 2\pi(e^4 - 1)\bar{x} = 4\pi \times \tfrac{1}{4}(3e^4 + 1)$

$$\Rightarrow \quad \bar{x} = \frac{(3e^4 + 1)}{2(e^4 - 1)}$$

$$= 1.54 \text{ (correct to 2 d.p.).}$$

The centre of mass is at $(1.54, 0)$.

Centres of mass of composite bodies

Once the positions of the centres of mass of standard solids have been found, it is possible to use these results to find the positions of the centres of mass of composite bodies. Some useful results are summarised in the following table.

Diagram	Body	Volume	Height of c.o.m. above base
	Solid sphere, radius r	$\frac{4}{3}\pi r^3$	r
	Solid hemisphere, radius r	$\frac{2}{3}\pi r^3$	$\frac{3}{8}r$
	Solid cone, height h, radius r	$\frac{1}{3}\pi r^2 h$	$\frac{1}{4}h$

You may also find it helpful to know the position of the centre of mass for some shells (hollow bodies with negligible wall thickness), and these are given below. A method for finding these is given in Mathematical note 4 (page 189).

Diagram	Body	Curved surface area	Height of c.o.m. above base
	Hollow hemisphere, radius r	$2\pi r^2$	$\frac{1}{2}r$
	Hollow cone, height h, radius r	$\pi r l$ $(l = \sqrt{r^2 + h^2})$	$\frac{1}{3}h$

EXAMPLE 4.5

(i) Find the position of the centre of mass of a uniform hemispherical bowl of thickness 1 cm and inside radius 9 cm.

(ii) A light handle AB of length 18 cm is attached to a point A on the rim of the bowl in such a way that the line AB passes through the centre of the hemisphere. What angle does AB make with the vertical when the bowl is hung from the end B?

SOLUTION

(i) Think of the bowl as a solid hemisphere of radius 10 cm from which another solid hemisphere of radius 9 cm has been removed. Then the original 10 cm hemisphere can be treated as a composite body, consisting of the bowl and the 9 cm hemisphere.

You can put all the information in a table.

10 cm hemisphere = bowl + 9 cm hemisphere

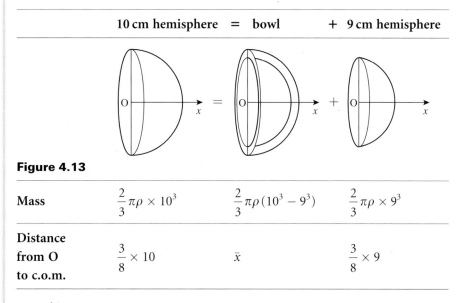

Figure 4.13

	10 cm hemisphere	bowl	9 cm hemisphere
Mass	$\frac{2}{3}\pi\rho \times 10^3$	$\frac{2}{3}\pi\rho(10^3 - 9^3)$	$\frac{2}{3}\pi\rho \times 9^3$
Distance from O to c.o.m.	$\frac{3}{8} \times 10$	$\bar{x}$	$\frac{3}{8} \times 9$

Taking moments gives

$$\left(\frac{2}{3}\pi\rho 10^3\right) \times \left(\frac{3}{8} \times 10\right) = \left(\frac{2}{3}\pi\rho(10^3 - 9^3)\right) \times \bar{x} + \left(\frac{2}{3}\pi\rho 9^3\right) \times \left(\frac{3}{8} \times 9\right)$$

This can be simplified by dividing through by $\frac{2}{3}\rho\pi$ to give

$$\frac{3}{8} \times 10^4 = (10^3 - 9^3)\bar{x} + \frac{3}{8} \times 9^4$$

$$\bar{x} = \frac{3(10^4 - 9^4)}{8(10^3 - 9^3)}$$

$$= 4.76 \text{ (to 3 s.f.)}.$$

(ii) The handle is light so the position of the centre of mass, G, is unchanged when it is attached. For equilibrium G must be vertically below B and the angle required is the angle ABG = α.

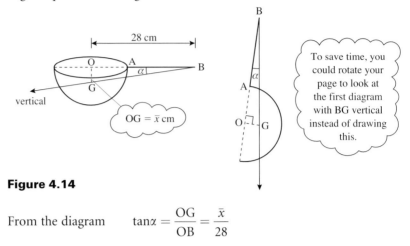

To save time, you could rotate your page to look at the first diagram with BG vertical instead of drawing this.

Figure 4.14

From the diagram $\qquad \tan\alpha = \dfrac{\text{OG}}{\text{OB}} = \dfrac{\bar{x}}{28}$

$$\Rightarrow \qquad \alpha = 9.65°$$

The angle between AB and the vertical is about 10°.

Note

An alternative, but equivalent method for finding $\bar{x}$ is to regard the bowl as the sum of a solid hemisphere of radius 10 cm and a solid hemisphere of radius 9 cm which has negative mass.

In this case the moments equation would be written

$$\frac{2}{3}\pi\rho(10^3 - 9^3)\bar{x} = \left(\frac{2}{3}\pi\rho 10^3\right) \times \left(\frac{3}{8} \times 10\right) + \left(-\frac{2}{3}\pi\rho 9^3\right) \times \left(\frac{3}{8} \times 9\right)$$

EXAMPLE 4.6

A traffic cone is modelled as a hollow cone of height 45 cm standing on a heavy cylindrical base of radius 20 cm and height 5 cm. The mass of the base is twice that of the cone.

(i) Find the position of the centre of mass of the traffic cone.

(ii) What is the angle of the steepest slope it can be placed on without toppling?

SOLUTION

(i) You can put the information in a table.

	Cone	Base	Together
Mass	m	$2m$	$3m$
Height of c.o.m. above O in cm	$\frac{1}{3} \times 45$ $+5$	$\frac{1}{2} \times 5$	$\bar{y}$

Figure 4.15

Then
$$20m + 5m = 3m\bar{y}$$
$$\Rightarrow \qquad \bar{y} = \frac{25}{3}$$

(ii) The cone begins to topple when the line GA is vertical.

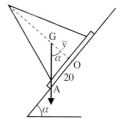

Then
$$\tan\alpha = \frac{20}{\bar{y}} = 2.4$$

The steepest slope is $\alpha = 67.4°$ to the horizontal.

Figure 4.16

1 In Exercise 4A question 1, you found the volumes of several solids of revolution produced by rotating certain regions through $360°$ about the x axis. These regions are described again below and the volumes of the resulting solids of revolution are given. In each case
   (a) draw a diagram of each solid showing an elementary disc at the point (x, y) on the curve
   (b) determine the position of its centre of mass by equating $V\bar{x}$ to a suitable integral.
   (i) $y = 2x$, the x axis and the lines $x = 1$ and $x = 3$ $\left(V = \frac{104\pi}{3}\right)$.
   (ii) $y = \sqrt{x}$, the x axis and the line $x = 4$ $(V = 8\pi)$.
   (iii) $y = 2x + 1$, the x axis and the lines $x = 1$ and $x = 5$ $\left(V = \frac{652\pi}{3}\right)$.
   (iv) $y = \dfrac{1}{x}$, the x axis and the lines $x = 1$ and $x = 3$ $\left(V = \frac{2\pi}{3}\right)$.
   (v) $y = 3e^x$, the x axis, the y axis and the line $x = 1.5$ $\left(V = \frac{9\pi}{2}(e^3 - 1)\right)$.
   (vi) $y = \cos x$ $\left(\text{from } x = 0 \text{ to } \frac{\pi}{2}\right)$, the x axis and the y axis $\left(V = \frac{\pi^2}{4}\right)$.

2 In Exercise 4A question 2, you found the volumes of several solids of revolution produced by rotating certain regions through $360°$ about the y axis. Some of these are described again below and their volumes are given. In each case
   (a) draw a diagram of each solid showing an elementary disc at the point (x, y) on the curve

(b) determine the position of its centre of mass by equating $V\bar{y}$ to a suitable integral.

(i) $y = x^3$, the y axis and the line $y = 8$ $\qquad\left(V = \dfrac{96\pi}{5}\right).$

(ii) $y = 2x - 1$, the y axis and the line $y = 5$ $\qquad(V = 18\pi).$

(iii) $x^2 + y^2 = 9$, the y axis and the line $y = 1$ and $y = 3$ $\quad\left(V = \dfrac{28\pi}{3}\right).$

3 (i) Sketch the curve $y = x^2(2 - x)$.

(ii) Find the volume of the solid formed when the closed region between the curve and the x axis is rotated about this axis.

(iii) Find the position of the centre of mass of this solid.

4 (i) Sketch the curve $y^2 = 4x$ (i.e. $y = \pm 2\sqrt{x}$) and shade the region between the curve, x axis and the lines $x = 1$ and $x = 4$.

(ii) Find the volume and the position of the centre of mass of the solid generated when the shaded region is rotated completely about the x axis.

(iii) The region between the same portion of the curve and the y axis is to be rotated through $360°$ about the y axis. Find

(a) appropriate limits for y

(b) the volume of revolution so formed

(c) the position of the centre of mass of this new solid of revolution.

5 (i) Sketch the ellipse $\dfrac{x^2}{9} + \dfrac{y^2}{4} = 1$ and shade the region lying between the curve and the axes for positive values of x and y.

(ii) Find the volume and centre of mass of the solid obtained by rotating the shaded region through $360°$ about the x axis.

6 Water fills a light hemispherical bowl of radius $12\,\text{cm}$ to a depth of $6\,\text{cm}$. Find the height of the centre of mass of the water above the base of the bowl.

7 A toy clown is modelled by a solid cone of radius r and height h, attached to a solid hemisphere of radius r and centre O as shown.

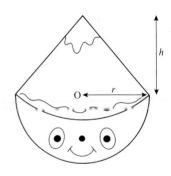

(i) Copy and complete the following table using the results on page 148.

	Clown	=	Cone	+	Hemisphere
Mass					
Distance of c.o.m. above O	$\bar{y}$				

(ii) Write down an equation for finding $\bar{y}$. (Divide by any common factors.)

(iii) If the centre of mass is at the centre of the hemisphere, use your equation to find the ratio of h to r.

(iv) If the ratio of h to r is less than that obtained in part (iii), what position will the toy assume when placed with a point on the hemisphere in contact with the ground?

8 The diagram shows a container consisting of a hollow cylinder of radius 3 cm and height 18 cm with a circular base, centre O, topped by a hollow cone of the same radius and height 4 cm. The container is made of thin, uniform material. The origin O is at the centre of the base.

(i) Copy and complete the following table using the results on page 148.

		Whole container	=	Cylinder base	+	Cylinder walls	+	Cone
Mass								
Distance of c.o.m. above O	$\bar{y}$							

(ii) Find the height of the centre of mass of the container above the base.

(iii) The container is placed with its circular base on a rough flat surface in a boat so that it cannot slip. If the boat heels over so that the surface makes an angle α to the horizontal, find at what value of α the empty container will topple over.

(iv) If the container is filled with liquid to the top of the cylinder, is it more or less likely to topple over than when it is empty? Give a reason for your answer.

9 The shape of the bowl of a wine glass is produced by rotating through $360°$ about the y axis the part of the curve $y = kx^2$ which lies between the origin and the line $y = h$.

(i) Draw a diagram of the bowl and, by integration, find the volume of the solid of revolution contained within it.

(ii) Show that the centre of mass of this solid is at the point $(0, \frac{2}{3}h)$ and hence write down its distance below the top of the glass. (Notice that this is independent of the value of k.)

(iii) The bowl of the glass can be modelled as a solid block of depth 9 cm with another similar block of depth 8.8 cm scooped out. Make out a table similar to that on page 149 using the results obtained in part (i). Show that the centre of mass of the bowl is 4.45 cm below the rim.

(iv) The complete wine glass can be modelled by a circular base of negligible thickness and radius 3 cm, a cylindrical stem of height 8 cm and the bowl (as above) of depth 9 cm. The masses of these three parts are in the ratio 1:1:2. Find the distance of the centre of mass of the whole glass from the circular base.

(v) If the glass is carried on a tray, what is the maximum angle to the horizontal that the tray can be held without the glass toppling over. You may assume that the glass does not slide.

10 The region in the x, y plane between the lines $x = h$, $y = 0$ and $y = kx$, shown in the diagram on the left, is rotated through $360°$ about the x axis to form a right circular cone C.

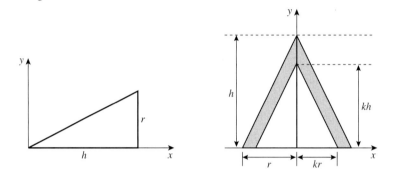

(i) Use calculus to prove that the volume of the cone C is $\frac{1}{3}\pi r^2 h$ and that the co-ordinates of the centre of mass are $\left(\dfrac{3h}{4}, 0\right)$.

A hollow cone B is formed by removing from C a similar smaller cone. The smaller cone removed has base radius kr and height kh, where $0 < k < 1$. This is shown in the diagram on the right with the cone B now standing upright with the centre of its base at the origin.

(ii) Show that the co-ordinates of the centre of mass of the hollow cone B are $\left(0, \dfrac{h(1 - k^4)}{4(1 - k^3)}\right)$

For a cone of small thickness, k is close to 1 and so may be written as $k = 1 - \varepsilon$, where ε is small.

(iii) Show that $k^3 = 1 - 3\varepsilon$ when ε is very small, and find a similar expression for k^4 in terms of ε.

(iv) Hence show that for a hollow cone made of uniform material of negligible thickness, the centre of mass is one third of the way from the centre of the base to the vertex.

[MEI]

11 A uniform solid is formed by rotating the region between the curve
$y = 2(1 - x^2)$ and the x axis between $x = -1$ and $x = 0$ through 2π radians
about the x axis, as shown in this diagram.

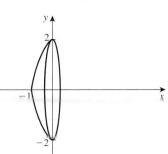

(i) Calculate the volume of the solid and show that the x co-ordinate of its
centre of mass is $-\frac{5}{16}$.

The solid is joined to a uniform solid cone of the same density, of radius 2
and height k, as shown in the next diagram.

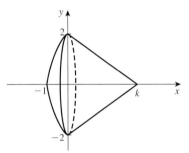

(ii) Show that the centre of mass of the combined solid has x co-ordinate
$$\frac{5(k^2 - 2)}{4(5k + 8)}.$$

The solid is placed on a rough plane inclined at $30°$ to the horizontal, as
shown in this diagram.

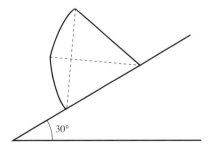

(iii) Determine whether the solid will topple in the cases

(a) $k = \sqrt{2}$

(b) $k = 2\sqrt{3}$.

Explain your reasoning carefully.

[MEI]

Centres of mass of plane regions

ACTIVITY

Find the position of the centre of mass of a semi-circular protractor by suspending it from one corner. In what ratio does it divide the axis of symmetry?

Vocabulary

A thin plane surface, like a protractor, is called a *lamina* (plural *laminae*). The laminae considered in this chapter are all uniform; that is they have the same mass per unit area, throughout. The *centroid* of a plane region is the centre of mass of a lamina of the same shape and negligible thickness.

Calculus methods for determining the centre of mass of a lamina

When a lamina or plane region is bounded by curves for which the equations are known, calculus methods can be used to find the position of its centre of mass in a similar manner to that used for volumes of revolution.

When a lamina occupies a region between a curve and the x axis, as shown in figure 4.17, it can be divided into elementary strips of width δx and length y. One such strip, situated at the point (x, y) on the curve, is shown. The dot indicates the centre of mass of this elementary strip. Let σ (the Greek letter sigma), be the *mass per unit area* of the lamina.

The length of the strip is y and its width is δx, so its mass δM is $\sigma y \delta x$.

The co-ordinates of the centre of mass of the strip are $(x, \frac{y}{2})$ so $\bar{x}$ can be found using

$$(\Sigma \delta M)\bar{x} = \Sigma(\delta M x)$$

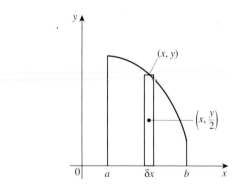

Figure 4.17

Substituting $\delta M = \sigma y \delta x$ in

$$(\Sigma \delta M) \bar{x} = \Sigma (\delta M x)$$

gives

$$(\Sigma \sigma y \delta x) \bar{x} = \Sigma (\sigma y \delta x \times x)$$

If the material is uniform, the mass per unit area is constant and so the equation can be divided through by σ. In that case,

$$(\Sigma y \delta x) \bar{x} = \Sigma (yx \delta x)$$

and in the limit as $\delta x \to 0$.

$$\left(\int_a^b y \, dx \right) \bar{x} = \int_a^b xy \, dx \qquad \text{①}$$

Notice that the first integral gives the area of the lamina.

You can find $\bar{y}$ in a similar way. Using the y co-ordinate, $\dfrac{y}{2}$, of the centre of the strip and dividing by σ as before:

$$(\Sigma y \delta x) \bar{y} = \Sigma \left(y \delta x \times \frac{y}{2} \right)$$

In the limit as $\delta x \to 0$ this becomes:

$$\left(\int_a^b y \, dx \right) \bar{y} = \int_a^b \frac{y^2}{2} \, dx \qquad \text{②}$$

The equations ① and ② can be combined to give the co-ordinates of the centre of mass of the lamina in the form of a position vector:

$$A \begin{pmatrix} \bar{x} \\ \bar{y} \end{pmatrix} = \begin{pmatrix} \displaystyle\int_a^b xy \, dx \\ \displaystyle\int_a^b \frac{y^2}{2} \, dx \end{pmatrix}$$

where A is the total area of the lamina or $\int_a^b y \, dx$.

⚠ Before deciding which formula to use, draw a diagram such as figure 4.17 so that you can see whether the formula you are using is sensible.

EXAMPLE 4.7

Find the position of the centre of mass of a uniform semi-circular lamina of radius r.

SOLUTION

The diagram below shows the lamina.

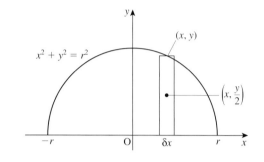

Figure 4.18

By symmetry, $\bar{x} = 0$

To find $\bar{y}$, use $\quad A\bar{y} = \int_a^b \dfrac{y^2}{2}\, dx.$

In this case, $A = \frac{1}{2}\pi r^2$ (because the lamina is a semi-circle), and the limits are $-r$ and $+r$.

Since the equation of the curve is $x^2 + y^2 = r^2$, you can write y^2 as $r^2 - x^2$.

This gives
$$\tfrac{1}{2}\pi r^2 \bar{y} = \int_{-r}^{r} \tfrac{1}{2}(r^2 - x^2)\, dx$$

$$= \tfrac{1}{2}\left[r^2 x - \frac{x^3}{3} \right]_{-r}^{r}$$

$$\Rightarrow \quad \tfrac{1}{2}\pi r^2 \bar{y} = \tfrac{1}{2}\left\{ \left(r^3 - \frac{r^3}{3} \right) - \left(-r^3 - \frac{(-r)^3}{3} \right) \right\}$$

$$= \tfrac{2}{3} r^3$$

$$\Rightarrow \quad \bar{y} = \frac{4r}{3\pi}$$

This is the distance of the centre of mass of the semi-circular lamina from its centre. It is roughly 0.4 times the radius. How does this compare with your own measurements in the Activity on page 156? They might differ slightly as a protractor has an extra strip along the diameter of the semi-circle.

EXAMPLE 4.8

Find the co-ordinates of the centroid of the region between the curve $y = 4 - x^2$ and the positive x and y axes.

SOLUTION

Figure 4.19

It is best to find the area, A, first. In this case:

$$A = \int y\,dx$$

$$= \int_0^2 (4 - x^2)\,dx$$

$$= \left[4x - \frac{x^3}{3}\right]_0^2$$

$$= (8 - \tfrac{8}{3}) - 0$$

$$= \frac{16}{3}$$

Then use $A\begin{pmatrix} \bar{x} \\ \bar{y} \end{pmatrix} = \begin{pmatrix} \displaystyle\int_0^2 xy\,dx \\[2mm] \displaystyle\int_0^2 \frac{y^2}{2}\,dx \end{pmatrix}$ to give

$$A\bar{x} = \int_0^2 (4 - x^2)x\,dx \quad \text{and} \quad A\bar{y} = \int_0^2 \frac{(4 - x^2)^2}{2}\,dx$$

$$= \int_0^2 (4x - x^3)\,dx \qquad\qquad = \int_0^2 \left(\frac{16 - 8x^2 + x^4}{2}\right)dx$$

$$= \left[\frac{4x^2}{2} - \frac{x^4}{4}\right]_0^2 \qquad\qquad = \frac{1}{2}\left[16x - \frac{8x^3}{3} + \frac{x^5}{5}\right]_0^2$$

$$= 4 \qquad\qquad\qquad\qquad = \frac{128}{15}$$

Substituting $A = \frac{16}{3}$ gives

$$\bar{x} = 4 \times \frac{3}{16} \quad \text{and} \quad \bar{y} = \frac{128}{15} \times \frac{3}{16}$$

$$\bar{x} = \frac{3}{4} = 0.75 \qquad \bar{y} = \frac{8}{5} = 1.6$$

The co-ordinates of the centroid are $(0.75, 1.6)$.

Using strips parallel to the x axis

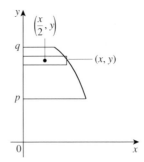

Figure 4.20

Sometimes it is necessary (or easier) to divide the region into strips parallel to the x axis as shown in figure 4.20. The area A is then $\int_p^q x\,dy$ and

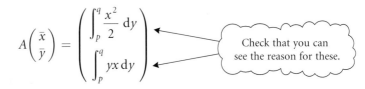

$$A\begin{pmatrix}\bar{x}\\\bar{y}\end{pmatrix}=\begin{pmatrix}\int_p^q\dfrac{x^2}{2}\,dy\\[2mm]\int_p^q yx\,dy\end{pmatrix}$$

Check that you can see the reason for these.

In this case the x in each integral should be written in terms of y. Where there is a choice between methods you should choose the one which gives the easiest integral to evaluate.

EXERCISE 4C

1 The regions (i) to (iv) below are all symmetrical about one axis and are defined in terms of the lines and curves which form their boundaries. For each region:

(a) Draw a sketch of the region and, using symmetry, write down one co-ordinate of the centroid G.

(b) Show on your diagram an elementary strip parallel to the y axis situated at the point (x, y) on the curve and mark a dot at its centre. Show the co-ordinates of this dot on your diagram.

(c) Write down the area of the strip in terms of x and δx.

(d) Use $A\bar{x} = \int xy\,dx$ or $A\bar{y} = \int \dfrac{y^2}{2}\,dx$, as appropriate, to find the other co-ordinate of G.

(i) The curve $y = 4 - x^2$ and the x axis.

(ii) The curves $y = e^x$ and $y = -e^x$, the y axis and the line $x = 1$.

(iii) The curve $y^2 = 4x$ (i.e. $y = \pm 2\sqrt{x}$) and the line $x = 4$. (Take care over the length of the strip.)

(iv) The curve $y = \sin x$ between $x = 0$ and $x = \pi$ and the x axis.

2 In the diagram, OAB is a uniform right-angled triangular lamina. OA = 6 cm and OB = 12 cm.

(i) Write down the area of the triangle.

(ii) Using OA as the x axis and OB as the y axis, find the equation of the line AB.

(iii) Find, by integration, the co-ordinates $(\bar{x}, \bar{y})$ of the centre of mass, G, of the triangle and verify that $\bar{x} = \frac{1}{3}$ OA and $\bar{y} = \frac{1}{3}$ OB.

3 (i) Find the equation of the straight line which meets the axes at the points A(a, 0) and B(0, b) and use integration to find the co-ordinates of the centre of mass of the triangle OAB.

(ii) The triangle PQR is divided into elementary strips parallel to QR as shown. Explain why the centre of mass, G, of triangle PQR lies on the median PP$'$.

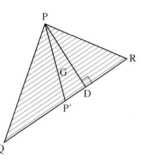

(iii) Now consider PQR to be made up of two right-angled triangles, PDQ and PDR. Use your answer to part (i) to explain why PG and GP$'$ are in the ratio 2:1. Draw a diagram to illustrate your answer.

4 (i) Sketch the curve $y = x^2(3 - x)$.

(ii) Find the co-ordinates of the centroid of the region between this curve and the x axis. (Note that this region is not symmetrical.)

5 (i) Draw a diagram showing the region R bounded by the curve $y^2 = 4x$ and the line $x = 4$. Mark on your diagram a strip parallel to the x axis, passing through a general point (x, y) on the curve.

(ii) Write down the area of the strip and the x co-ordinate of its centroid.

(iii) Use your answer to part (ii) to form a suitable integral and, by integrating with respect to y, find the centre of mass of the region R.

In questions 6 to 8 you can use the result for the position of the centre of mass of a semi-circle found on page 158. It is at a distance $\dfrac{4r}{3\pi}$ from the centre.

6

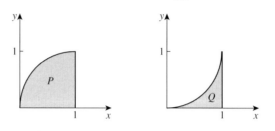

(i) The region P of a uniform lamina satisfies the inequalities $(x-1)^2 + y^2 \leqslant 1$, $0 \leqslant x \leqslant 1$, and $y \geqslant 0$ (i.e. P is a quadrant of a circle of radius 1 and centre $(1, 0)$ as shown in the diagram above left). Find $\bar{y}$ for P and hence show that the co-ordinates of the centre of mass of P are $\left(\dfrac{3\pi - 4}{3\pi}, \dfrac{4}{3\pi} \right)$.

(ii) The region Q of a uniform lamina satisfies the inequalities $y \leqslant x^2$, $0 \leqslant x \leqslant 1$ and $y \geqslant 0$, as shown in the diagram above right. Find the co-ordinates of the centre of mass of Q.

The uniform lamina R is obtained by taking the region P defined above and then removing the region Q, as shown in the diagram below.

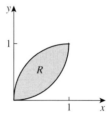

(iii) Find the co-ordinates of the centre of mass of R, referred to the axes shown in the diagram above, giving your answer correct to three decimal places.

[MEI]

7 A letter P is made up from a rectangle and a semi-circle with a smaller semi-circle cut out as shown.

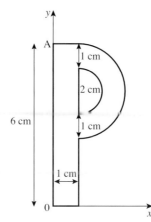

(i) Taking O as the origin, write down the areas of the component parts of the letter, and the co-ordinates of their centres of mass.

(ii) Find the co-ordinates of the centre of mass of the letter.

(iii) What angle will AO make with the vertical if the letter is hung from the corner A?

8 (i) Draw a diagram to show the circle $x^2 + y^2 = 4$ and the line $x = 1$.

(ii) Without using integration, show that the area of the minor segment of the circle $x^2 + y^2 = 4$ which is cut off by the line $x = 1$ is

$$A = \frac{4\pi}{3} - \sqrt{3}$$

(iii) Find the x co-ordinate of the centre of mass of this segment by finding a suitable integral between the limits 1 and 2.

(iv) A crescent is formed by removing a segment of this shape from a semi-circle of radius $\sqrt{3}$ units. Find the position of the centre of mass of this crescent.

(v) Find also the angle between the diameter of the semi-circle and the vertical when the crescent is hung from one end of this diameter.

9 The diagram shows a uniform lamina OAB in the shape of the region between the curve $y = kx^{\frac{3}{2}}$, the x axis and the line $x = 1$, where k is a positive constant.

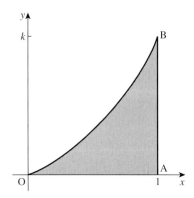

(i) Show, by integration, that the co-ordinates of the centre of mass of the lamina are $\left(\frac{5}{7}, \frac{5}{16}k\right)$.

The lamina is suspended from the vertex A and hangs in equilibrium as shown in the next diagram. The angle that AB makes with the vertical is denoted by θ.

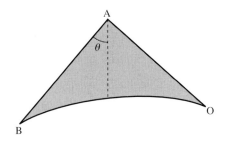

(ii) Find $\tan \theta$ in terms of k.

(iii) Calculate the value of k for which O is at the same horizontal level as B.

[**MEI**]

10 A uniform lamina is made in the shape of the region between the curve $y = \frac{1}{2}k(1 - x^2)$ and the x axis, as shown in the diagram.

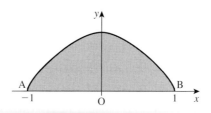

(i) Show that the centre of mass of the lamina is at $(0, \frac{1}{5}k)$.

A uniform lamina is made for an exhibition sign in the form of the shape in part (i) attached to a rectangle ABCD, where AB = 2 and BC = 1. The sign is suspended by two vertical wires attached at A and D as shown in the next diagram.

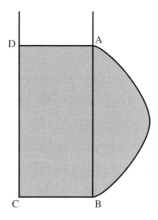

(ii) Show that the centre of mass of the sign is at a distance

$$\frac{2k^2 + 10k + 15}{10k + 30}$$

from the mid-point of CD.

(iii) The tension in the wire at A is twice the tension in the wire at D. Calculate k.

[MEI]

Stability

A solid body is made of a hemisphere with a cone of the same radius attached to its plane surface. Where should its centre of mass be so that it will

(i) always return to the upright position when knocked over?

(ii) always roll over on to its conical surface when slightly disturbed from the upright position?

Assuming that the density of the body is uniform and that it is placed on a horizontal surface, find a relationship between AO and OB in each case.

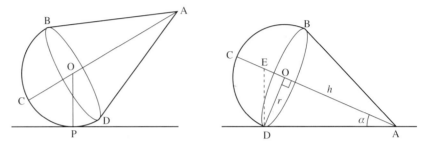

Look at the cases where the centre of mass is

(a) between A and O

(b) between O and E (Hint: show that OE $= r\tan\alpha$)

(c) between E and C.

What will happen if the body is placed on a sloping surface?

Rolling

Carefully place an egg near the edge of a rectangular tray or board and gently lift this edge. Notice how the egg rolls. Most eggs will roll in a curve.

How can you make one roll in a straight line?

What can you say about the position of the egg's centre of mass when it does roll in a straight line?

Investigate the manner in which different objects such as a ball, a cylinder, a coin, an apple and a cone (or part of a cone such as a plant pot) roll on a smooth surface.

What makes a body roll in a curved line rather than a straight one?

The balls used in the game of bowls are solids of revolution which are designed to roll in curves. Contrary to popular belief they are not weighted in any way.

1 Volumes of revolution

- About the x axis:

$$V = \int_a^b \pi y^2 \, dx$$

- About the y axis:

$$V = \int_p^q \pi x^2 \, dx$$

2 Centres of mass of uniform bodies

For a volume of revolution

- About the x axis:

$$\left(\int_a^b \pi y^2 \, dx \right) \bar{x} = \int_a^b \pi x y^2 \, dx$$

$$\text{and} \quad \bar{y} = 0$$

- About the y axis:

$$\bar{x} = 0 \quad \text{and}$$

$$\left(\int_p^q \pi x^2 \, dy \right) \bar{y} = \int_p^q \pi y x^2 \, dy$$

For a uniform plane lamina, area A, as shown in the diagrams

- $A = \int_a^b y \, dx$

- $A \begin{pmatrix} \bar{x} \\ \bar{y} \end{pmatrix} = \begin{pmatrix} \int_a^b xy \, dx \\ \int_a^b \dfrac{y^2}{2} \, dx \end{pmatrix}$

- $A = \int_p^q x \, dy$

- $A \begin{pmatrix} \bar{x} \\ \bar{y} \end{pmatrix} = \begin{pmatrix} \int_p^q \dfrac{x^2}{2} \, dy \\ \int_p^q yx \, dy \end{pmatrix}$

5

Dimensions and units

But whatever his weight in pounds, shillings and ounces,
He always seems bigger because of his bounces.

The House at Pooh Corner, A.A. Milne

What makes the above rhyme about Tigger sound so ridiculous?

Look at the units in the first line of the rhyme. Pounds can be units of either money or mass, shillings are units of money and ounces are units of mass. You can see at once that not only is there a mixture of units, but also of the underlying quantities which they are measuring.

In this chapter you will look at the quantities which you have met in mechanics and classify them according to their *dimensions*. The dimensions of a quantity are closely related to the units in which it is measured.

All of the quantities you have met so far can be described in terms of three fundamental quantities, Mass, Length and Time. Take, for example, the quantity *area*; there are many familiar ways of finding area, depending on the shape involved (see figure 5.1).

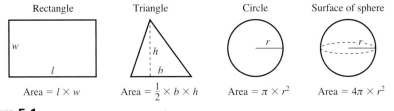

Rectangle	Triangle	Circle	Surface of sphere
Area = $l \times w$	Area = $\frac{1}{2} \times b \times h$	Area = $\pi \times r^2$	Area = $4\pi \times r^2$

Figure 5.1

All of these formulae have essentially the same form:

 area = number × length × length.

In the case of the rectangle the 'number' is 1 and the two 'lengths' are the length and breadth of the shape. For the circle and the sphere the two 'lengths' are the same, namely the radius, and the 'numbers' are multiples of π. However, the structure of the formula is the same for all four shapes, and indeed for any other area formula you can think of (for example, the area of a trapezium or the surface area of a cone).

The dimensions of the quantity Area can therefore be summarised using the formula

$$[\text{Area}] = \text{L}^2.$$

The square brackets [ ] mean *the dimensions of,* and the letter L represents the quantity Length. So the whole statement reads:

The dimensions of area = Length squared.

There are two important points to notice about this.

1 The numbers at the start of the formulae (in the four cases above they are 1, $\frac{1}{2}$, π and 4π) do not feature in the dimensions of the quantity because they are *dimensionless.*

2 The units in which a quantity is measured are derived directly from its dimensions. In the S.I. system the unit of length is 1 metre. Since the dimensions of area are L^2, it follows that the S.I. unit for area is 1 metre squared, usually written m^2.

Note

The area under a curve is often found by calculus methods, using the formula

area $= \int y\,dx.$

In this case both y and the infinitesimal quantity dx represent lengths and so the integral has dimensions L^2, as must be the case since it represents an area.

 How many formulae can you find for the volumes of objects?

Show that all your formulae for volume involve multiplying three lengths together so that

$[\text{Volume}] = L^3.$

The dimensions of further quantities

So far the quantities discussed, area and volume, have only involved lengths. What are the dimensions of speed (or velocity), and of acceleration?

To find the dimensions of any quantity, start by writing down a simple formula which you might use to calculate it. For example, to calculate speed you might use

$$\text{Speed} = \frac{\text{Distance}}{\text{Time}}.$$

The dimensions follow immediately from this. A distance is clearly a length, so

$$[\text{Speed}] = \frac{[\text{Distance}]}{[\text{Time}]} = \frac{L}{T} = LT^{-1}$$

It follows that the S.I. unit for speed is 1 metre per second, written ms^{-1}. Notice that a second fundamental dimension, T (Time), is now involved.

Similarly $\qquad$ Acceleration $= \dfrac{\text{Change in velocity}}{\text{Time taken}}$

and so $\qquad$ $[\text{Acceleration}] = \dfrac{[\text{Speed}]}{[\text{Time}]}$

$$= \dfrac{LT^{-1}}{T}$$

$$= LT^{-2}$$

The corresponding S.I. unit is therefore $1 \, \text{ms}^{-2}$.

Exactly the same procedure allows you to find the dimensions of force.

$$\text{Force} = \text{Mass} \times \text{Acceleration}$$
$$[\text{Force}] = [\text{Mass}] \times [\text{Acceleration}]$$
$$= M \times LT^{-2}$$
$$= MLT^{-2}.$$

Therefore the S.I. unit for force is 1 kilogram metre per second squared. Because force is an important concept and this unit would be such a mouthful, it is given a name of its own, the newton (N).

$$1 \, \text{N} = 1 \, \text{kg ms}^{-2}.$$

Notice that now all three of the basic dimensions, M, L and T are being used.

EXAMPLE 5.1

(i) Find the dimensions of

(a) kinetic energy

(b) gravitational potential energy

(c) work.

(ii) Comment on the significance of your answers.

SOLUTION

(i) (a) $\qquad$ Kinetic energy $= \frac{1}{2}mv^2$
$$[\text{K.E.}] = M \times (LT^{-1})^2$$
$$= ML^2T^{-2}$$

(b) Gravitational potential energy $= mgh$
$$[\text{P.E.}] = M \times LT^{-2} \times L$$
$$= ML^2T^{-2}$$

g is an acceleration so it has dimensions LT^{-2}

(c) $\qquad$ Work $= \text{Force} \times \text{Distance}$
$$= MLT^{-2} \times L$$
$$= ML^2T^{-2}$$

(ii) All three have the same dimensions because they are examples of the same underlying quantity, energy. The S.I. unit for this could be written as $1 \, \text{kg m}^2\text{s}^{-2}$ but is actually given the special name of 1 joule, J.

Dimensionless quantities

Some quantities have no dimensions. For example, angles are dimensionless. The angle θ in figure 5.2 is defined as

$$\theta(\text{radians}) = \frac{\text{arc length}}{\text{radius}}$$

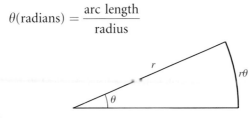

Figure 5.2

Consequently $\qquad [\theta] = \dfrac{L}{L}$

and θ is dimensionless.

Notice that although in this case the formula used gave θ in radians, the same result would have been obtained for θ in degrees, using

$$\theta = 360 \times \frac{\text{arc length}}{2\pi \times \text{radius}}.$$

The dimensions of a quantity cannot be altered by changing the units in which it is measured.

All numbers are dimensionless, including the trigonometrical ratios, for example $\sin\theta$, $\cos\theta$, $\tan\theta$, and irrational numbers such as π and e. This is the reason why you ignore any numbers in a formula when considering its dimensions; numbers, being dimensionless, cannot be included in this analysis.

Other systems of units

The units used in this chapter, and indeed in all the books in this series, are almost entirely S.I. units. There are other self-consistent sets of units, such as the 'cgs' system (centimetre, gram, second) or the Imperial system (foot, pound, second). Knowing the dimensions of a quantity allows you to find the appropriate unit within any system.

The set of dimensions may also be extended to include quantities that arise in electricity and magnetism. For instance Q represents the dimension of electrical charge.

Change of units

It is helpful to know the dimensions of a quantity when you are changing the units in which it is to be measured, as in the following example.

EXAMPLE 5.2

The energy of a body is 5000 foot poundals (imperial units based on feet, pounds and seconds). Write this in S.I. units, i.e. joules.
(To 3 s.f., 1 pound (lb) = 0.453 kg and 1 foot = 0.305 m.)

SOLUTION

The dimensions of energy are $ML^2T^{-2} = \dfrac{ML^2}{T^2}$

So
$$1 \text{ foot poundal} = \frac{1 \text{ lb} \times (1 \text{ foot})^2}{(1 \text{ second})^2}$$

$$= \frac{0.453 \text{ kg} \times (0.305 \text{ m})^2}{(1 \text{ second})^2}$$

$$= 0.0421 \text{ J}$$

and
$$5000 \text{ foot poundals} = 5000 \times 0.0421 \text{ J}$$

$$= 211 \text{ J (to 3 s.f.)}.$$

EXERCISE 5A

Draw up a table like the one below, and, having copied the first two lines, extend it to cover the following quantities.

Speed, acceleration, *g*, force (= mass × acceleration), weight, kinetic energy, gravitational potential energy, work, power, impulse, momentum, pressure (= force/area), density, moment, angle, angular velocity, angular acceleration, modulus of elasticity, stiffness, gravitational constant (*G*), period, frequency, coefficient of restitution, coefficient of friction.

Quantity	Formula	Dimensions	S.I. unit
Area	$l \times w$	L^2	m^2
Volume	$l \times w \times h$	L^3	m^3

You may find it helpful to keep the completed table somewhere handy for reference.

Dimensional consistency

In any equation or formula, all the terms must have the same dimensions. If that is the case, the equation is said to be *dimensionally consistent*. If not, for example if force and area are being added or subtracted, or if a mass is being equated to a velocity, the equation is said to be dimensionally inconsistent.

Any statement that is dimensionally inconsistent *must* be wrong. In the rhyme at the start of this chapter, the phrase '*his weight in pounds, shillings and ounces*' is nonsense because it is dimensionally inconsistent.

EXAMPLE 5.3

Show that the formula

$$s = ut + \tfrac{1}{2}at^2$$

is dimensionally consistent.

SOLUTION

There are three terms, with dimensions as follows:

$$[s] = L$$
$$[ut] = LT^{-1} \times T = L$$
$$\left[\tfrac{1}{2}at^2\right] = LT^{-2} \times T^2 = L$$

All three terms have the same dimensions, and so the formula is dimensionally consistent.

The fact that a formula is dimensionally consistent does not mean it is necessarily right, but if it is dimensionally inconsistent it is certainly wrong.

Good mathematicians develop the habit of automatically checking the dimensional consistency of anything they write. A consequence of this is that they tend to leave everything written in symbols until the final calculation. You know, for example, that g has dimensions LT^{-2} but if it is replaced by an approximate value, e.g. 10, its dimensions are no longer evident: $h = \tfrac{1}{2}gt^2$ is dimensionally consistent but $h = 5t^2$ seems not to be.

EXAMPLE 5.4

A mathematician writes down the equation

$$\tfrac{1}{2}m_1v_1{}^2 = m_2gh + m_2v_2.$$

Show that it must be wrong.

SOLUTION

Checking for dimensional consistency:

$$\left[\tfrac{1}{2}m_1v_1{}^2\right] = M \times (LT^{-1})^2 \quad = ML^2T^{-2}$$
$$[m_2gh] = M \times LT^{-2} \times L = ML^2T^{-2}$$
$$[m_2v_2] = M \times LT^{-1} \quad\quad = MLT^{-1}.$$

The third term is dimensionally different from the other two and so the equation is incorrect.

Finding the form of a relationship

It is sometimes possible to determine the form of a relationship just by looking at the dimensions of the quantities likely to be involved, as in the following example.

A pendulum consists of a light string of length l with a bob of mass m attached to the end. You would expect that the period, t, might depend in some way on the variables l and m, and also on the value of g.

This can be expressed in the form

$$t = kl^{\alpha}m^{\beta}g^{\gamma}$$

where k is dimensionless and the powers α, β and γ are to be found.

Writing down the dimensions of each side gives

$$T = L^{\alpha} \times M^{\beta} \times (LT^{-2})^{\gamma}$$

$$T = L^{\alpha+\gamma}M^{\beta}T^{-2\gamma}.$$

The left-hand side of the equation, T, may be written as $L^0M^0T^1$ and so

$$L^0M^0T^1 = L^{\alpha+\gamma}M^{\beta}T^{-2\gamma}.$$

Equating the powers of L, M and T gives:

$$
\begin{aligned}
\text{L:} \quad & 0 = \alpha + \gamma \\
\text{M:} \quad & 0 = \beta \\
\text{T:} \quad & 1 = -2\gamma
\end{aligned}
$$

Solving these gives $\alpha = \frac{1}{2}$, $\beta = 0$ and $\gamma = -\frac{1}{2}$ and so the relationship is

$$t = k\sqrt{\frac{l}{g}}.$$

You may remember that you derived this formula in the chapter on simple harmonic motion on page 116. You found it in the form

$$t = 2\pi\sqrt{\frac{l}{g}}.$$

That result was obtained by writing down the equation of motion of the pendulum bob and comparing it with the equation for simple harmonic motion. In this method all you had to do was to think about the dimensions, a very beautiful piece of mathematics. Of course the dimensions method does not tell you that the value of k is 2π, but it does provide the correct form of the relationship.

Notice that the mass of the pendulum bob, m, does not feature in the formula for the period. This is found to be the case in practice: a heavier bob makes no difference to the period.

What about the angle of swing of the pendulum, θ? Since angles are dimensionless it cannot feature in this argument. You may like to think of its effect as being included within the dimensionless k. In fact the value of k is approximately constant (equal to 2π) for small values of θ, but it does vary with θ for larger swings.

In the next example the work is taken a step further. First the form of a relationship is proposed, then data are used to determine the constant involved. The resulting formula is used to predict the outcome of a future experiment. Notice that the units look after themselves providing you are consistent with their use; in this case they happen to be in the cgs system.

EXAMPLE 5.5

In an experiment, small spheres are dropped into a container of liquid which is sufficiently deep for them to attain terminal velocity. For any sphere, the terminal velocity, V, is thought to depend on its radius, r, its weight mg and the viscosity of the liquid, η (the Greek letter 'eta'). (Viscosity is a measure of the 'stickiness' of a liquid and has dimensions $ML^{-1}T^{-1}$.)

(i) Write down a formula for V as the product of unknown powers of r, mg, η, and a dimensionless constant k.

(ii) Find the powers of r, mg and η and write out the formula for V with these values substituted in.

In a particular liquid it is found that a sphere of mass 0.02 g and radius 0.1 cm has terminal velocity 5 cm s^{-1}.

(iii) Find the value of $\dfrac{k}{\eta}$ taking g to be 1000 cm s^{-2}.

(iv) Find the terminal velocity of a sphere of mass 0.03 g and radius 0.2 cm.

SOLUTION

(i) $V = kr^{\alpha}(mg)^{\beta}\eta^{\gamma}$

(ii) Taking dimensions of both sides of the equation gives

$$LT^{-1} = L^{\alpha} \times (MLT^{-2})^{\beta} \times (ML^{-1}T^{-1})^{\gamma}$$
$$M^0L^1T^{-1} = M^{\beta+\gamma}L^{\alpha+\beta-\gamma}T^{-2\beta-\gamma}$$

Equating powers: M: $0 = \beta + \gamma$
          L: $1 = \alpha + \beta - \gamma$
          T: $-1 = -2\beta - \gamma$

Solving these gives $\alpha = -1$, $\beta = 1$ and $\gamma = -1$

and so the formula is $V = \dfrac{kmg}{r\eta}$ ①

(iii) Substituting $m = 0.02$, $r = 0.1$, $g = 1000$ and $V = 5$ gives

$$5 = \frac{k \times 0.02 \times 1000}{0.1 \times \eta}$$
$$\frac{k}{\eta} = 0.025 \quad \text{(in cgs units)}.$$

(iv) Substituting $m = 0.03$, $r = 0.2$, $g = 1000$ and $\dfrac{k}{\eta} = 0.025$ in ①

gives
$$V = \frac{0.025 \times 0.03 \times 1000}{0.2}$$
$$= 3.75$$

The terminal velocity of this sphere is $3.75\ \text{cm s}^{-1}$.

The method of dimensions

This method for finding the form of a proposed formula is sometimes called *the method of dimensions*; at other times it is simply referred to as *dimensional analysis*. There are a number of points which you should realise when using it.

1 In mechanics, relationships are based on three fundamental quantities Mass, Length and Time and so the right-hand side of the formula can involve no more than three independent quantities. Otherwise you will end up with three equations to find four or more unknown powers. (The last example actually involved four quantities, m, g, r and η, but the first two of these were tied together as the weight, mg, and were not, therefore, independent.)

2 The method requires you to make modelling assumptions about which quantities are going to be important and which can be ignored. You must **always be prepared to review these assumptions**.

3 This method can only be used when a quantity can be written as a product of powers of other quantities. There are many situations which cannot be modelled by this type of formula and for these situations this method is not appropriate. For example, the formula $s = ut + \frac{1}{2}at^2$ has two separate terms which are added together on the right-hand side. The form of this relationship could not be predicted using the method of dimensions.

EXERCISE 5B

1 Check the dimensional consistency of each of the formulae below and hence state whether it could be correct or is definitely wrong. You may assume that all letters have their conventional meanings.

(i) $v^2 - u^2 = 2as$

(ii) $x = \dfrac{(m_1 x_1 + m_2 x_2)}{m_1 + m_2}$

(iii) $F - mg = ma$

(iv) $T_1 - T_2 = \frac{1}{2}mv^2$ (T_1 and T_2 are tensions)

(v) $Fs = mv - mu$

(vi) $mg\sin\alpha - \mu mg\cos\alpha = ma$

(vii) $m_1 gd_1 - m_2 gd_2 = (m_1 + m_2)a$

(viii) $\frac{1}{2}mv^2 = \frac{1}{2}mu^2 + mgh\sin\theta$

(ix) $v^2 = \omega^2 a^2 - x^2$ (a is amplitude)

(x) $\frac{1}{2}F(u + v) = \dfrac{(v^2 - u^2)}{2t}$

2 A scientist thinks that the speed, v, of a wave travelling along the surface of an ocean depends on the depth of the ocean, h, the density of the water in the ocean, ρ (the Greek letter 'rho'), and g.

(i)   Write down the dimensions of each of the quantities v, h, ρ and g.

The scientist expresses his idea using the formula

$$v = kh^{\alpha}\rho^{\beta}g^{\gamma} \quad \text{where } k \text{ is dimensionless.}$$

(ii) Use dimensional analysis to find the values of α, β and γ and write out the formula with these values substituted in.

(iii) Do waves travel faster in deep water or shallow water?

(iv) Do waves travel faster in winter (when the water density is greater) or in summer?

3 A water container has a hole in the bottom. When it is filled to a depth d it takes time t for the water to run out. The time t may be modelled as the product of powers of d and g and a dimensionless constant k.

(i)   Write down a formula for t.

(ii) Use dimensional analysis to find the powers of d and g in the formula.

When the container is filled to a depth of 0.4 m it takes 30 s to empty.

(iii) Taking g to be $10\,\text{ms}^{-2}$, find the value of k.

(iv) How long does it take the container to empty when it is filled to a depth of 60 cm?

4 (i)   Write down the dimensions of energy.

A student who has not yet learnt about the energy of rotating bodies observes a symmetrical flywheel of mass m and radius r rotating in a horizontal plane about a vertical axis through its middle with angular speed ω. The student decides that the rotational energy, E, of the flywheel can only depend on a product of powers of these three quantities and a dimensionless constant.

(ii) Express the student's opinion in the form of a formula for E.

(iii) Use dimensional analysis to find the powers of m, r and ω in the formula.

The student conducts some experiments which show that when $m = 20\,\text{kg}$, $r = 0.5\,\text{m}$ and $\omega = 4\,\text{rad s}^{-1}$, $E = 40\,\text{J}$.

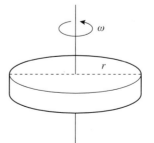

(iv) Given that the student's experiments are accurate, find the complete formula for E.

(v) A similar flywheel, mounted in the same way, has mass 50 kg and radius 1.2 m. Find its energy when it is rotating at $12\,\mathrm{rad\,s^{-1}}$.

5 A ball of mass m travelling with velocity v vertically downwards hits a horizontal surface and bounces back up, rising to a height h. The coefficient of restitution between the ball and the surface is e.

(i) Use the definition of coefficient of restitution to show that e is dimensionless.

It is believed that h depends on a product of powers of v, m and g and a dimensionless constant, so a formula is proposed of the form

$$h = kv^{\alpha}m^{\beta}g^{\gamma} \quad \text{where } k \text{ is dimensionless.}$$

(ii) Use dimensional analysis to find the values of α, β and γ, and write down the formula with these values substituted in.

(iii) Two balls, identical in all respects except that one is heavier than the other, fall with equal speeds. Explain how your answer to part (ii) allows you to decide which (if either) bounces higher.

(iv) The height h clearly does depend on e also. Why was it not considered useful to include it in the formula?

(v) Use your knowledge of mechanics to find a formula for h in terms of v, m, g and e.

(vi) Explain the relationship between k in the answer to part (ii) and e.

6 The magnitude of the force of gravitational attraction, F, between two objects of mass m_1 and m_2 at a distance d apart is given by

$$F = \frac{Gm_1 m_2}{d^2}$$

where G is the universal constant of gravitation.

(i) Find the dimensions of G.

An astronomer proposes a model in which the lifetime, t, of a star depends on a product of powers of its mass, m, its initial radius r_0, G and a dimensionless constant.

(ii) Use the method of dimensions to find the resulting formula for t.

Observation shows that the larger the initial radius the longer the lifetime of the star, but that the larger the mass the shorter the lifetime of the star.

(iii) Is the model consistent with these observations?

(iv) Show that the model can be expressed more simply if the initial density, ρ_0, of the star is used as one of the variables.

7 The volume rate of flow R (in $m^3 s^{-1}$) of a liquid with a viscosity η (in $kg\,m^{-1}s^{-1}$) through a cylindrical pipe of length a (in m) and an internal radius r (in m) is believed to be of the form

$$R = k\eta^w a^x r^y P^z,$$

where k is a non-dimensional constant and P (in Nm^{-2}) is the pressure difference between the ends of the pipe.

Using dimensional considerations
(i)   show that $w = -1$ and $z = 1$
(ii) find the relationship between x and y.

Observations of a water supply provided at constant pressure and viscosity produced the following recordings:

Pipe length, a (m)	100	200
Internal radius, r (m)	0.050	0.050
Flow rate, R ($m^3 s^{-1}$)	0.420	0.210

(iii) Derive a formula for R in terms of a and r for such a supply.
(iv) Find the rate of flow of water through 1000 m of pipe with an internal radius of 0.075 m under the same pressure and with the same viscosity.

[MEI]

8 In an investigation into viscosity small spheres are allowed to fall from rest through a column of a viscous liquid and their terminal speeds are measured. It is believed that the terminal speed V of a sphere depends upon a product of powers of its weight mg, its radius r and the viscosity η of the liquid and a dimensionless constant.
(i)   Given that the dimensions of viscosity are $ML^{-1}T^{-1}$ use the method of dimensions to establish the form of the relationship for V in terms of m, r, η and g.
(ii) The mass m of the sphere may be written in terms of its radius r and its density ρ. Write down this relationship.
(iii) Using parts (i) and (ii) write down a relationship for V in terms of ρ, r, η and g.
(iv) A steel sphere of radius 0.15 cm and density $7.8\,g\,cm^{-3}$ falls through a column of a viscous liquid and is found to have a terminal speed of $6.0\,cm\,s^{-1}$. A lead sphere of density $11.4\,g\,cm^{-3}$ falling through the same liquid is found to have a terminal speed of $5.0\,cm\,s^{-1}$. Determine the radius of the lead sphere.

[MEI]

9 **(i)** Define π and hence find its dimensions.

(ii) Newton's law of universal gravitation states that the magnitude of the force F on a point mass m_1 due to the presence of a point mass m_2 at a distance r is given by

$$F = \frac{Gm_1m_2}{r^2}$$

Find the dimensions of G.

(iii) The constant G has a value 6.67×10^{-11} in S.I. units. An astronomer proposes a system of units based upon the mass of the earth, M_e, its radius, R_e, and the time it takes for one revolution about the sun, T_e. Given that $M_e = 6.98 \times 10^{24}$ kg, $R_e = 6.37 \times 10^6$ m and $T_e = 3.16 \times 10^7$ s, find the value of G in terms of these earth units.

(iv) Comment briefly upon the different natures of the constants π and G.

[MEI]

10 In the early seventeenth century Mersenne (1588–1648) conducted experiments with long lengths of rope and so obtained the law for the frequency of transverse vibrations of strings.

Assuming that the frequency depends on products of powers of T, the tension in the rope, l, the length of the rope, and m, the mass per unit length of the rope,

(i) find, by dimensional analysis, the form of the relationship.

A rope of length 24 m and mass 0.5 kg m^{-1} under tension of 72 N is found to vibrate with a frequency of $\frac{1}{4}$ of a cycle per second.

(ii) State the exact relationship between the frequency, T, l and m.

(iii) Find the frequency of vibration of a string of length 20 cm and mass 0.005 g cm^{-1} under a tension of 8×10^5 dynes. (The dyne is the cgs unit of force: 1 dyne is the force required to give a mass of 1 g an acceleration of 1 cm s^{-2}.)

11 An artillery officer is conducting a series of experiments to find the maximum range, R, of a gun which fires shells from ground level across level ground.

(i) Show, by considering the shell as a projectile with initial velocity u at an angle to the horizontal and ignoring air resistance, that

$$R = \frac{u^2}{g} \sin 2\alpha$$

and that this has a maximum value, R_M, when α is 45°.

(ii) Show that the expression for R in part (i) is dimensionally consistent.

The officer finds that the shells fall some distance short of their predicted range. Deciding that this must be due to air resistance, he proposes a model in which the magnitude of the force of resistance, F, is proportional to the speed of the shell, v:

$$F = cv.$$

(iii) Show that the constant c is not dimensionless and write down its dimensions.

The officer then suggests that a better model for the range of the shell, when fired at 45° to the horizontal, is given by:

$$R = R_M(1 - \varepsilon)$$

where ε (epsilon) is a number less than 1 representing the proportion of the range which is lost.

(iv) State the dimensions of ε.

The officer believes that ε depends on a product of powers of the speed of projection u, the constant c, g and the mass m of the shell.

(v) Use dimensional analysis to find an expression for ε in which the power of u is 1. Express the improved model as a formula for R.

It is suggested that a more accurate and more general model still would have the form

$$R = R_M(1 + a_1\varepsilon + a_2\varepsilon^2 + a_3\varepsilon^3 + \ldots)$$

where $a_1, a_2, a_3, \ldots$ are dimensionless coefficients, taking into account (among other things) the angle of projection. (Clearly, a_1 would be negative.)

(vi) Show that such a model is dimensionally consistent.

12 For a wave travelling with speed c, the wavelength is denoted by λ and the frequency, which is the number of complete oscillations per second, by f.

(i) Verify that the relation $c = \lambda f$ is dimensionally consistent.

For a sound wave travelling in either air or water, the frequency, f, depends on the wavelength, λ, the density, ρ, and the pressure, P. [Pressure is force per unit area.]

(ii) State the dimensions of P and ρ.

(iii) Assuming a relation of the form $f = K\lambda^\alpha P^\beta \rho^\gamma$, find the values of α, β and γ given that K is a dimensionless constant with a different value for air and water. How can the value of K be found?

The speed of propagation, c, of a sound wave is known to be given by

$$c = \sqrt{\frac{AP}{\rho}} \text{ where } A = 1.4 \text{ for air.}$$

(iv) By using this expression for c and the equation in part (i), find the value of K for sound waves in air.

(v) It is observed that the density of water is much greater than the density of air and that the speed of sound in water is much greater than in air. What does this imply about the value of A for water? Explain your answer.

[MEI]

13 A simple pendulum consists of a particle of mass m attached to the end of a light inextensible string of length l. The particle is held with the string taut and slightly displaced from the vertical. It is then released and the period of the resulting small oscillations is believed to be of the form $k_1 m^\alpha l^\beta g^\gamma$ where k_1 is a dimensionless constant.

(i) Use dimensional analysis to determine α, β and γ.

The pendulum is now set in motion as a conical pendulum so that the particle moves in a horizontal circle with constant angular velocity ω. The string makes a constant angle θ with the vertical throughout the motion as shown in the diagram.

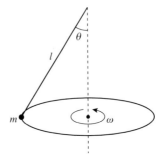

(ii) For a particular value of θ, the period for one revolution of a conical pendulum is believed to depend only on m, l and g. Explain why the period will be of the form $k_2 \sqrt{\dfrac{l}{g}}$ where k_2 is a dimensionless constant.

An expression for k_2 is to be found from the equations of motion for the conical pendulum.

(iii) Find an expression for ω^2 in terms of l, g and θ. For what range of values of ω^2 is the motion possible?

(iv) Find an expression for k_2 in terms of θ. Given that for the simple pendulum in part (i) $k_1 = 2\pi$, which motion has the longer period? Explain your reasoning.

[MEI]

14 (i) State the dimensions of density and angular velocity. Show that the dimensions of power are ML^2T^{-3}.

The power P required to drive a propeller of diameter d at an angular velocity ω in a fluid of density ρ is believed to obey a law of the form

$$P = k_1 d^\alpha \omega^\beta \rho^\gamma$$

where k_1 is a dimensionless constant.

(ii) Determine the values of α, β and γ.

It is suggested that the viscosity, η, of the fluid should be included in the equation. The formula

$$P = k_2 d^\alpha \omega^\beta \rho^\gamma \left(\frac{\omega \rho d^2}{\eta} \right)^\delta \qquad \text{①}$$

is proposed. In this formula, k_2 is a dimensionless constant; α, β and γ have the same values as in part (ii); δ is unknown.

(iii) The quantity $\dfrac{\omega \rho d^2}{\eta}$ is dimensionless. Find the dimensions of η.

Explain briefly whether it is possible to find the value of δ from equation ①.

Equation ① can be used to scale results from a model propeller to a full-size propeller. For the model, $d = 0.6$, $\rho = 1000$ and $\eta = 0.001$, all measured in S.I. units. For the full-size propeller, $d = 1.8$, $\rho = 850$ and $\eta = 0.012$, again all measured in S.I. units.

To enable ① to be used, $\dfrac{\omega \rho d^2}{\eta}$ must have the same value for both the model and the full-size propeller.

(iv) If the full-size propeller is to be run at $25 \, \text{rad s}^{-1}$, calculate the angular velocity of the model propeller.

At this speed, the model requires 3 kW of power.

(v) Calculate the power required by the full-size propeller.

[MEI]

15 An experiment consists of stretching a length of wire and fixing its ends. The wire is then plucked to produce transverse vibrations. The frequency of these vibrations, f, is modelled by the equation

$$f = kP^\alpha l^\beta z^\gamma$$

where P is the tension in the wire, l is the length of the stretched wire, z is the mass per unit length of the stretched wire and k is a dimensionless constant.

(i) Given that the dimensions of frequency are T^{-1}, use dimensional analysis to show that $\alpha = \frac{1}{2}$, $\beta = -1$ and $\gamma = -\frac{1}{2}$.

Two pieces of wire, A and B, used in the experiment both have modulus of elasticity 500 N.

(ii) Piece A has natural length 0.9 m and stretched length 0.945 m. Calculate the tension in the wire.

(iii) Piece B is stretched to a length of 0.81 m. The tension in the wire is 40 N. Calculate the natural length of the wire.

(iv) *In their unstretched state*, the two wires had the same mass per unit length. In the experiment, wires A and B produce frequencies f_A and f_B respectively. Calculate the ratio $f_A : f_B$.

[MEI]

Fundamental quantities

The system of dimensions you have met in this chapter describes the quantities relevant to mechanics on a human scale in a consistent and altogether satisfactory manner. When, however, these concepts are applied at the scale of the whole universe, difficulties arise; cosmology is a set of unresolved problems. Is it possible that we are looking at the universe in terms of the wrong basic quantities?

It is suggested that three more appropriate quantities might be: mass, energy and momentum, corresponding to the laws of conservation of mass, conservation of energy and conservation of momentum.

(i) Show that such a system would be inadequate.

(ii) Suggest and investigate an alternative system in which one of the quantities is replaced by another which might be considered fundamental.

The definition of force

The system of dimensions worked out in this chapter depends on the assumption that force is defined by the equation $F = ma$. An alternative definition is given by Newton's law of gravitation.

$$F = \frac{Gm_1m_2}{d^2}.$$

Suppose that instead this law is taken as the definition of force, so that in suitable units,

$$F = \frac{m_1m_2}{d^2},$$

and Newton's second law is regarded as secondary to this, so that it is written

$$F = kma.$$

What would be the dimensions of k, using the M, L, T system?

Investigate the effect of this change of definition on the dimensions of some other quantities commonly used in mechanics. Do you consider such a change to be desirable?

KEY POINTS

1 Any quantity in mechanics may be expressed in terms of the three fundamental dimensions:

  mass, M; length, L; time, T.

2 The unit for any quantity is derived from the three fundamental dimensions.

3 Numbers are dimensionless.

4 All formulae and equations must be dimensionally consistent.

5 Using dimensional analysis you can sometimes find the form of a relationship as the product of powers of the quantities involved, and a dimensionless constant.

Mathematical notes

1 Velocity and acceleration for motion in a circle

When a particle moves in a circle, it is convenient for the velocity and acceleration to be expressed in the radial and transverse (tangential) directions. For this reason, unit vectors $\hat{\mathbf{r}}$ and $\hat{\boldsymbol{\theta}}$ are defined in these two directions. Unlike the unit vectors $\mathbf{i}$ and $\mathbf{j}$, however, these vectors are not constant. They change in direction as the particle moves round the circle.

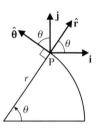

Figure A1

Figure A1 shows $\hat{\mathbf{r}}$ and $\hat{\boldsymbol{\theta}}$ when the particle P is at a general position. You can see that

$$\hat{\mathbf{r}} = \cos\theta\mathbf{i} + \sin\theta\mathbf{j}$$

and $\qquad \hat{\boldsymbol{\theta}} = -\sin\theta\mathbf{i} + \cos\theta\mathbf{j}$

Differentiating $\hat{\mathbf{r}}$ with respect to time,

$$\frac{\mathrm{d}\hat{\mathbf{r}}}{\mathrm{d}t} = \frac{\mathrm{d}}{\mathrm{d}t}(\cos\theta)\mathbf{i} + \frac{\mathrm{d}}{\mathrm{d}t}(\sin\theta)\mathbf{j}$$

$$= -\sin\theta\frac{\mathrm{d}\theta}{\mathrm{d}t}\mathbf{i} + \cos\theta\frac{\mathrm{d}\theta}{\mathrm{d}t}\mathbf{j}$$

$$= (-\sin\theta\mathbf{i} + \cos\theta\mathbf{j})\dot{\theta} \quad \text{where } \dot{\theta} = \frac{\mathrm{d}\theta}{\mathrm{d}t}.$$

You will recognise that the vector in brackets, $(-\sin\theta\mathbf{i} + \cos\theta\mathbf{j})$, is the same as $\hat{\boldsymbol{\theta}}$, the unit vector in the transverse direction. Consequently,

$$\frac{\mathrm{d}\hat{\mathbf{r}}}{\mathrm{d}t} = \dot{\theta}\hat{\boldsymbol{\theta}}.$$

Similarly, $\qquad \dfrac{\mathrm{d}\hat{\boldsymbol{\theta}}}{\mathrm{d}t} = -(\cos\theta)\dot{\theta}\mathbf{i} - (\sin\theta)\dot{\theta}\mathbf{j}$

$$= -(\cos\theta\mathbf{i} + \sin\theta\mathbf{j})\dot{\theta}$$

i.e. $\qquad \dfrac{\mathrm{d}\hat{\boldsymbol{\theta}}}{\mathrm{d}t} = -\dot{\theta}\hat{\mathbf{r}}.$

These two results, $\dfrac{\mathrm{d}\hat{\mathbf{r}}}{\mathrm{d}t} = \dot{\theta}\hat{\boldsymbol{\theta}}$ and $\dfrac{\mathrm{d}\hat{\boldsymbol{\theta}}}{\mathrm{d}t} = -\dot{\theta}\hat{\mathbf{r}}$ are very important, and apply to all motion described in polar co-ordinates, not just circular motion.

In the case of circular motion with radius r, the displacement from the centre at any time is $r\hat{\mathbf{r}}$.

Differentiating this with respect to time, you obtain

$$\text{velocity} = \frac{\mathrm{d}r}{\mathrm{d}t}\hat{\mathbf{r}} + r\frac{\mathrm{d}\hat{\mathbf{r}}}{\mathrm{d}t}$$

$$= 0 + r\dot{\theta}\hat{\boldsymbol{\theta}} \quad \text{(since } r \text{ is constant)}$$

$$= r\dot{\theta}\hat{\boldsymbol{\theta}} \quad \text{(i.e. } r\dot{\theta} \text{ in the transverse direction)}.$$

Differentiating again you obtain

$$\text{acceleration} = \frac{\mathrm{d}r}{\mathrm{d}t}\dot{\theta}\hat{\boldsymbol{\theta}} + r\frac{\mathrm{d}\dot{\theta}}{\mathrm{d}t}\hat{\boldsymbol{\theta}} + r\dot{\theta}\frac{\mathrm{d}\hat{\boldsymbol{\theta}}}{\mathrm{d}t}$$

$$= 0 + r\ddot{\theta}\hat{\boldsymbol{\theta}} - r\dot{\theta}^2\hat{\mathbf{r}}$$

Thus the acceleration has two components:

transverse: $\quad r\ddot{\theta}$
radial: $\qquad -r\dot{\theta}^2$.

2 Solving the differential equation for SHM

Simple harmonic motion has been defined by the differential equation

$$\ddot{x} = -\omega^2 x.$$

Several forms of the solution of this equation, involving sine and cosine functions, have been used in Chapter 3. The work which follows shows you how this equation is solved to obtain the general solution in the form $x = a\sin(\omega t + \varepsilon)$. You have seen in Chapter 3 that other forms of the solution are equivalent to this.

The acceleration, $\ddot{x} = \dfrac{\mathrm{d}v}{\mathrm{d}t}$, can be written by using the chain rule as

$$\frac{\mathrm{d}v}{\mathrm{d}x} \times \frac{\mathrm{d}x}{\mathrm{d}t} = v\frac{\mathrm{d}v}{\mathrm{d}x} \qquad \text{①}$$

This is a useful result when acceleration is given in terms of x (or v).

So the SHM equation becomes

$$v\frac{\mathrm{d}v}{\mathrm{d}x} = -\omega^2 x$$

Separating the variables gives:

$$\int v\,\mathrm{d}v = \int -\omega^2 x\,\mathrm{d}x$$

$$\Rightarrow \quad \frac{v^2}{2} = -\frac{\omega^2 x^2}{2} + c$$

Let the amplitude be a, so that $v = 0$ when $x = a$.

Then $\qquad 0 = -\dfrac{\omega^2 a^2}{2} + c \qquad \Rightarrow \qquad c = +\dfrac{\omega^2 a^2}{2}$

Therefore $\qquad\qquad v^2 = \omega^2(a^2 - x^2)$

It follows from this that: $\qquad v = \pm\omega\sqrt{a^2 - x^2} \qquad \Rightarrow \qquad \dfrac{dx}{dt} = \pm\omega\sqrt{a^2 - x^2}$

Separating the variables gives: $\qquad \displaystyle\int \dfrac{dx}{\pm\sqrt{a^2 - x^2}} = \int \omega\, dt = \omega t + k$

For the positive square root in the integral on the left-hand side use the substitution $x = a\sin u$, $dx = a\cos u\, du$.

Then $\qquad\qquad \displaystyle\int \dfrac{dx}{\sqrt{a^2 - x^2}} = \int \dfrac{a\cos u\, du}{a\cos u}$

$$= u = \arcsin\left(\dfrac{x}{a}\right)$$

In this case:

$$\arcsin\left(\dfrac{x}{a}\right) = \omega t + \varepsilon \quad \text{where } \varepsilon \text{ is the constant of integration, } k$$

$$\Rightarrow \quad x = a\sin(\omega t + \varepsilon) \qquad\qquad ②$$

For the negative root use $x = a\cos u$ to give $\arccos\left(\dfrac{x}{a}\right)$ for the left-hand integral.

In this case:

$$\arccos\left(\dfrac{x}{a}\right) = \omega t + \varepsilon_1 \qquad (\text{now } k = \varepsilon_1)$$

$$\Rightarrow \quad x = a\cos(\omega t + \varepsilon_1) \qquad\qquad ③$$

As you saw in Chapter 3, the two forms ② and ③ are equivalent.

3 The work–energy equation for a variable force

You can use the acceleration in the form given in equation ① on page 187 to prove the work–energy equation for a particle moving in a straight line under a variable force as follows.

$$ma = F$$

$$\Rightarrow \quad mv\dfrac{dv}{dx} = F$$

$$\Rightarrow \quad \int mv\, dv = \int F\, dx$$

If $v = u$ when $x = 0$, this gives

$$\tfrac{1}{2}mv^2 - \tfrac{1}{2}mu^2 = \int_0^x F\, dx$$

This is the definition of the work done by a variable force F over a displacement x. Compare with the work done in stretching a spring on page 66

The increase in kinetic energy of the particle is equal to the work done by the force.

4 The centre of mass of a shell

It is possible to find the position of the centres of mass of thin shells by using formulae already obtained for solid bodies. A hemispherical shell, for example, can be formed by removing a small hemisphere (say H_1) from a larger one (H_2). Suppose that the radii of the two hemispheres are a and b respectively.

$$H_2 \qquad = \qquad \text{shell} \qquad + \qquad H_1$$

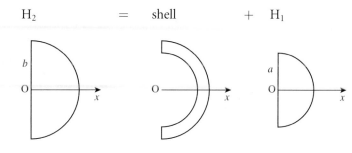

Figure A2

Mass $\qquad \frac{2}{3}\pi\rho b^3 \qquad\qquad \frac{2}{3}\pi\rho(b^3 - a^3) \qquad\qquad \frac{2}{3}\pi\rho a^3$

Distance of $\qquad \frac{3}{8}b \qquad\qquad\qquad \bar{x} \qquad\qquad\qquad \frac{3}{8}a$

c.o.m. from O

This gives the equation:

$$\frac{2}{3}\pi\rho b^3(\tfrac{3}{8}b) = \frac{2}{3}\pi\rho(b^3 - a^3)\bar{x} + \frac{2}{3}\pi\rho a^3(\tfrac{3}{8}a)$$

$$(b^3 - a^3)\bar{x} = b^3(\tfrac{3}{8}b) - a^3(\tfrac{3}{8}a)$$

$$\Rightarrow \quad \bar{x} = \frac{3(b^4 - a^4)}{8(b^3 - a^3)} \qquad\qquad ①$$

This is the position of the centre of mass of a shell of any thickness. The position of the centre of mass of a thin shell of radius a, can be found by letting $b = a + h$, and then letting $h \to 0$.

It is necessary to expand $(a + h)^4$ and $(a + h)^3$ using the binomial theorem:

$$\text{Then} \quad b^4 - a^4 = (a + h)^4 - a^4$$

$$= (a^4 + 4a^3h + 6a^2h^2 + 4ah^3 + h^4) - a^4$$

$$= h(4a^3 + 6a^2h + 4ah^2 + h^3)$$

and similarly: $\qquad b^3 - a^3 = (a + h)^3 - a^3$

$$= h(3a^2 + 3ah + h^2)$$

Then

$$\bar{x} = \frac{3(b^4 - a^4)}{8(b^3 - a^3)}$$

$$= \frac{3h(4a^3 + 6a^2h + 4ah^2 + h^3)}{8h(3a^2 + 3ah + h^2)}$$

Cancelling h and then letting $h \to 0$ gives $\bar{x}$ for the shell:

$$\bar{x} = \frac{3}{8} \times \frac{4a^3}{3a^2} = \frac{a}{2}.$$

Answers

Chapter 1

❓ (Page 1)

Forces which pull them towards the centre of the circle.
Gravity pulls it in.
It moves off at a tangent.
No

❓ (Page 3)

They are often given in radians per second and one turn is 2π radians.

Exercise 1A (Page 4)

1 (i) $8.2 \, \text{rad s}^{-1}$
  (ii) $4.7 \, \text{rad s}^{-1}$
  (iii) $3.5 \, \text{rad s}^{-1}$
2 $2865 \, \text{rpm}$
3 (i) (a) $0.033 \, \text{rpm}$
    (b) $0.0035 \, \text{rad s}^{-1}$
  (ii) $0.24 \, \text{ms}^{-1}$
4 $32.5 \, \text{rad s}^{-1}$
5 (i) $50 \, \text{rad s}^{-1}$
  (ii) $150 \, \text{rad s}^{-1}$
6 (i) $3820 \, \text{rpm}$
  (ii) $2080 \, \text{rpm}$
7 (i) $1.99 \times 10^{-7} \, \text{rad s}^{-1}$
  (ii) $7.27 \times 10^{-5} \, \text{rad s}^{-1}$
  (iii) $465 \, \text{ms}^{-1}$
  (iv) about $290 \, \text{ms}^{-1}$ at latitude $51.5°$
8 $2.29:1$
9 (i) 61.71
  (ii) points on a large object would travel with different speeds
10 (i) big: $2.09 \times 10^{-3} \, \text{ms}^{-1}$, small: $1.16 \times 10^{-4} \, \text{ms}^{-1}$
  (ii) $18:1$ the radius is also involved
11 (i) $4.91 \, \text{m}$
  (ii) $12.3 \, \text{ms}^{-1}$
12 (i) $v = 2\cos t\mathbf{i} - 2\sin t\mathbf{j} - \frac{1}{2}\mathbf{k}$
  (ii) $|v| = \sqrt{4.25} = 2.06 \, \text{ms}^{-1}$
  (iii) $a = -2\sin t\mathbf{i} - 2\cos t\mathbf{j}$; magnitude $2 \, \text{ms}^{-2}$ horizontally towards the vertical axis
13 $\sqrt{\dfrac{5000\pi}{t + 144.5\pi}}$; assuming radius increases steadily, not in steps with each wrap round.

14 (i) no
  (ii)

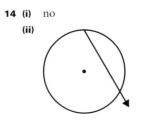

❓ (Page 9)

(i) $0 \, \text{ms}^{-1}$ so $u = r\omega$
(ii) $\dfrac{u}{r}$
(iii) $2u \, \text{ms}^{-1}$ forwards and $\sqrt{2}u \, \text{ms}^{-1}$ at $45°$ to the forward direction.

❓ Activity (Page 15)

When you rotate fast enough, the coin flies off the card. When the card is tilted it stays put at higher angular speeds.

❓ (Page 16)

See text that follows.

❓ (Page 18)

1 Resolve perpendicular to the slope
$$R - mg\cos\alpha = M\frac{v^2}{r}\sin\alpha.$$ Then parallel to the slope. No slipping down if
$$mg\sin\alpha - F = M\frac{v^2}{r}\cos\alpha,$$ and $F < \mu R$. No slipping up if $mg\sin\alpha + F = M\dfrac{v^2}{r}\cos\alpha$, and $F < \mu R$.
Substitute for F and R and rearrange.

2 The bend is safe at 30 mph. In general bends are safer for larger r. So long as $\mu > \tan\alpha$, there is no lower limit for v and then α can be increased in order to increase the upper limit.

Exercise 1B (Page 20)

1 (i) Neither, both have $\omega = 0.75 \, \text{rad s}^{-1}$.
  (ii) No because they have the same angular speed.
  (iii) $13.5 \, \text{ms}^{-2}$, $11.25 \, \text{ms}^{-2}$
  (iv) towards the centre for circular motion

2 (i) (a) neither slips

(b) B slips, A doesn't

(c) both slip

(ii) A slips first, radius matters, mass doesn't matter

3 (i) accelerates because direction changes

(ii) $11.25\ \text{ms}^{-2}$

(iii) $2250\ \text{N}$

(iv) No, outside wheels go faster so force is greater

4 (i) T for fixed seats

(ii) F, as $v = r\omega$ so speed depends on r.

(iii) F, as $a = r\omega^2$ so acceleration depends on r.

5 (i) (a) $0.5\ \text{rad s}^{-1}$

(b) $1\ \text{ms}^{-2}$

(c) $60\ \text{N}$ towards centre

(ii) skater is particle

6 B has greater force because greater acceleration

7 (i) (a) $\dfrac{(2 \times 10^7)}{\sqrt{r}}$ (3 s.f.)

(b) $\pi r^{\frac{3}{2}} \times 10^{-7}\ \text{s}$

(ii) $T^2 = \pi^2 \times 10^{-14}\ r^3$

(iii) $4.23 \times 10^7\ \text{m}$

8 (i) $5.71 \times 10^{-3}\ \text{ms}^{-2}$

(ii) $1.77 \times 10^{30}\ \text{kg}$

(iii) any planet in this orbit would have the same period whatever its mass

9 (i) vertical force required to balance weight

(ii) $12.57\ \text{rad s}^{-1}$

(iii)

(iv) $T\sin\theta = mr\omega^2 = 0.18 \times 0.8\sin\theta \times 12.57^2$;

$T\cos\theta = mg = 1.764$

(vi) $22.8\ \text{N}$

10 (i) $263\ \text{N}$

(ii) The weight of the sphere is very small compared with the tension in the cord.

(iii) $23\ \text{ms}^{-1}$

11 (i) $6272\ \text{N}$

(a) The car is about to skid on a bend.

(b) The car is accelerating or braking and is about to skid.

(ii) $69\ \text{mph}\ (30.7\ \text{ms}^{-1})$

(iii)

(iv) $R\sin\alpha = \dfrac{mv^2}{r}$, $R\cos\alpha = mg$

(vi) $10.8°$ or $0.189\ \text{rad}$

12 (i) $44\ \text{mph}\ (19.8\ \text{ms}^{-1})$

(ii) $4\ \text{mph}\ (1.82\ \text{ms}^{-1})$ faster

13 (i) $\pi\ \text{rad s}^{-1}$, $5\pi\ \text{ms}^{-1}$

(iii) $40.1\ \text{rpm}$

(iv) $102\ \text{m}$

14 (i) $\dfrac{\pi}{30}\ \text{rad s}^{-1}$

(ii) $\dfrac{\pi}{3}\ \text{ms}^{-1}$

(iii) no transverse acceleration

(iv) $40\,g\cos\theta - R\cos\phi = \frac{4}{9}\pi^2$

(v) $384, 30.3°$

15 (i) $\cos\alpha > \cos\beta \Rightarrow \alpha < \beta$

so $x > 2a - x$

$x > a$

16 (i) $\dfrac{\pi}{60}\ \text{rad s}^{-1}$

(ii)

$L\cos 26° - Mg = 0$

$L\sin 26° = Mr\omega^2$

$r = 1743\ \text{m}$

(iv)

A wheel detaching at any point P lands at Q where $PQ = 1446\ \text{m}$.

$C_1Q = \sqrt{r^2 + PQ^2} = 2265\ \text{m}$ for all positions of P.

Exercise 1C (Page 29)

1 (i) $0.02\ \text{rad s}^{-2}$

(ii) $900\ \text{rad}$

2 (i) $6.28\ \text{rad s}^{-2}$

(ii) $4\ \text{revs}$

3 **(i)** 4 rad s^{-1}

(ii) 0.0005 rad s^{-2}

(iii) 16 000 rad

(iv) 32 000 m

4 9.42 ms^{-1}

5 **(i)** area = total angle turned through

(ii) 13.5 revolutions, 254 m

(iii) 1.18 ms^{-2}

(iv) 0.03 π ms^{-2} vertically upwards and 0.03 π^2 ms^{-2} horizontally towards the centre

❓ (Page 35)

No, see text that follows

❓ Activity (Page 36)

If the string breaks the object will fly off at a tangent to the circle. If a rod were used rather than a string the motion would be the same for 1 and 2. For 3, when a string is used the object leaves the circle and falls in a parabola. On a rod it swings back as a pendulum.

❓ (Page 39)

Pressure on your finger as the car goes by because the track is pushed up by the equal and opposite force of the car acting on it.

❓ (Page 39)

$T = mr\omega^2 - mg\cos\alpha$, but $R = mg\cos\beta - mr\omega^2$ so $T > 0$ if ω is sufficiently large and $R > 0$ if ω is sufficiently small.

❓ (Page 41)

(i) and (iv)

Exercise 1D (Page 43)

1 **(i)** A: 4 ms^{-2} B: 40 ms^{-2}

(ii) **(a)** A yes, B no

(b) A no, B yes

(c) A no, B yes

(d) A yes, B yes

2 **A** **(i)** 22.2m J

(ii) complete revolutions; 4.98 ms^{-1}

(iii) **(a)** 73.8m N towards O

(b) 15m N towards O

B **(i)** 18m J

(ii) stops; 1.84 m

(iii) **(a)** 18m N towards O

(b) 9m N away from O

C **(i)** 4.74m J

(ii) stops; 0.48 m

(iii) **(a)** 6.49m N away from O

(b) 9.49m N away from O

3 **(i)** 0.186mg J

(iv) 0.598 m

(v) No, it leaves the track

4 **(i)** 0.8g J, 6.35 ms^{-1}

(ii) $\sqrt{9 + 1.6g(1 - \cos\theta)}$

(iii) **(a)** 0.725 N

(b) 30.125 N

(iv)

$T = 15.43 - 14.7\cos\theta$, $g\sin\theta$

5 **(i)** 82 ms^{-1}, 53 ms^{-1}

(ii) 67.8 ms^{-2}, 28.6 ms^{-2}

(iii)

$R_1 = 5432$ N, $R_2 = 1316$ N

(iv) He would fail to complete the loop

(v) 138 m

6 **(i)** 15 cm

(ii) 3.45 rad s^{-1}

(iii) about 1.9 rad s^{-2}

(iv) Girl let go before reaching the vertical.

7 **(i)** almost zero speed at the top of the loop not sufficient

(ii) 20 m

(iii) it stops below the centre and returns to C; 8 m

8 (i) $12\,\text{ms}^{-1}$, 27 mph

(ii) Traffic used to travel more slowly.

(iii) Increase the radius by making the approaches less steep.

9 (i) K.E. $= \frac{1}{2} \times 200 \times 21^2 = 44\,100$

The energy equation including K.E. and P.E. gives

$$200g \times 20 + \frac{1}{2} \times 200v^2 = 44\,100$$
$$v = 7\,\text{ms}^{-1}$$

(ii) radial acceleration $= \dfrac{7^2}{10}$

$$= 4.9$$

$$R + mg = m \times 4.9$$
$$R = -980\,\text{N}$$

Force from track is up so could not operate.

(iii) $\frac{1}{2} \times 200v^2 + 200g \times 15 = 44\,100$

$$v^2 = 147$$

radial acceleration $= \dfrac{147}{10} = 14.7\,\text{ms}^{-2}$

transverse acceleration $= g\sin 120 = \dfrac{\sqrt{3}}{2}g\,\text{ms}^{-2}$

$$\tan \alpha = \dfrac{\frac{\sqrt{3}}{2}g}{14.7} = \dfrac{1}{\sqrt{3}}$$

$$\alpha = 30° = \text{angle OBA}$$

10 (i) $v^2 = gl(2\cos\theta - 1)$

(iii) $2mg$ when $\theta = 0$

(iv) Perpendicular to AB

(v) $\dfrac{\pi}{6}$

Chapter 2

❓ (Page 51)

Use energy considerations. See the investigation at the end of this chapter.

Exercise 2A (Page 56)

1 (i)

(ii) $6.125\,\text{Nm}^{-1}$

(iii) $12.25\,\text{N}$

2 (i) $20\,\text{N}$

(ii) $20\,\text{N}$

(iii) Tension required to double the length is the same. There is a 20 N force at the fixed end in part (i).

3 (i) $0.03\,\text{N}$

(ii) $0.04\,\text{m}$

(iii) $0.45\,\text{m}$

(iv) 0.1125

4 (i) $4.9\,\text{N}$

(ii) $61.25\,\text{Nm}^{-1}$

(iii) $0.625\,\text{kg}$

(iv) $1.2\,\text{m}$

5 (i) $30\,\text{N}$

(ii) 3

(iii) $300\,\text{Nm}^{-1}$

(iv) Spring becomes fully compressed with fewer than seven blocks.

6 $\dfrac{ka}{k - m\omega^2}\,\text{m}$

Exercise 2B (Page 60)

1 (i) $60\,\text{N}$

(ii) $0.04\,\text{m}$

(iii) $2400\,\text{N}$; could be two strings together

2 (i) $12\,000\,\text{N}$

(ii) $80\,000\,\text{Nm}^{-1}$

(iii) $0.05\,\text{m}$

(iv) $0.02\,\text{m}$

3 (i) $7000\,\text{N}$

(ii) $7000\,\text{N}$, $10\,000\,\text{Nm}^{-1}$

(iii) $4000\,\text{N}$

4 (i) $198\,\text{N}$

(ii) $654\,\text{N}$

(iii) 118%

(iv) $51.6\,\text{m}$

5 (i) $T = F$ for each spring, $\dfrac{F}{k_1}$, $\dfrac{F}{k_2}$

6 (i) $(0.3 - x)\,\text{m}$

(ii) $16x\,\text{N}$, $25(0.3 - x)\,\text{N}$

(iii) 0.183

7 (i) $2.2 - h$ m, $h - 1.2$ m

(ii) $44 - 20h$ N, $30h - 36$ N

(iii) 1.2

(iv) 20 N, 0 N

8 (i) $\dfrac{l_0}{\lambda} mg\sin\alpha$

(ii) (a) $\dfrac{l_0}{\lambda} mg (\mu\cos\alpha + \sin\alpha)$

(b) $\dfrac{l_0}{\lambda} mg (\sin\alpha - \mu\cos\alpha)$

9 (i) 1000 N

(ii) 0.024 m

(iii) $R = 5000h - 730$

10 (ii) 0.306 m

(iii) An elastic string is unlikely to pass smoothly over a peg.

11 (i) 5.1 kg

(ii) 0.8784 m

(iii) 59.8 N

(iv) 3.52

12 (i) (b) $\dfrac{g}{80n}$ m

(iii) 4

(iv) 0.098 m

Exercise 2C (Page 70)

1 (i) 0.1 J

(ii) 0.001 J

(iii) 0.4 J

(iv) 0 J

2 (i) 4 J

(ii) 0.25 J

(iii) 1 J

(iv) 0.0625 J

3 (i) 0.75 J

(ii) 5.48 ms^{-1}

4 (i) $0.006\,67$ J

(ii) 0.577 ms^{-1}

5 (i) 5×10^4 J

(ii) 7.07 ms^{-1}

(iii) 1.29 m

(iv) 7.07×10^4 N, 35.4 ms^{-2}

(v) Truck moves back along the rail at 5 ms^{-1} if other forces ignored.

6 0.433 m, 0.067 m

7 (i) B is in equilibrium

(ii) 0.8 m, 6 N

(iii) 2.7 J

(iv) 10 ms^{-1}

8 (i) 562.5 J

(ii) 0.15

(iii) 0.8 ms^{-1}

(iv) $1440 = 25\,000x_1^2 + 20\,000x_2^2$, $5x_1 = 4x_2$, $x_1 = 0.16$, $x_2 = 0.2$

9 (ii) $2\sqrt{5}a$

(iv) mga

(v) P.E. lost $= 7mga$.

Energy is not conserved because the mass is lowered by some external force.

10 (i) 0.4, 1

(ii) It does not go slack.

(iii) 1.125 m

Exercise 2D (Page 76)

1 (i) $5h^2$ J

(ii) $0.2gh$ J

(iii) 0.392

2 $2l_0$

3 $l_0\left(1 + \dfrac{mg}{\lambda}\right)$

4 (ii) 0.1294

5 0.463 m

6 (i) 1 J

(iii) 0.2 m

7 (i) 0.1098 m

(ii) 0.149 m

9 (i) $\arccos\left(\dfrac{g}{\omega^2 l}\right)$

(ii) $\arccos\left(\dfrac{g(k - m\omega^2)}{\omega^2 l_0 k}\right)$

10 (i) 0.8 m

(ii) $98(x - 0.5)$ N, $98(2 - x)$ N

(iii) 57.3 J

(iv) 0.81 ms^{-1}

11 (i) $\dfrac{mg}{k}$

(ii) $mg\left(l_0 + \dfrac{mg}{k}\right)$

(iii) $\dfrac{m^2 g^2}{2k}$

(iv) (ii) > (iii), external work done to move block

(v) $\dfrac{mg}{M}$

12 (iii) -122 ms^{-2}

13 (i) 0.96 m

(ii) 0.69 m

(iii) 0.036 kg

(iv) 0.75 m

(v) (a) Closer: h increases when m decreases.

(b) Closer: h increases as E.P.E. increases.

? (Page 80)

$20.3\,\text{ms}^{-2}$ for a person weighing 90 kg. A lighter person would feel a greater deceleration, approximately $27\,\text{ms}^{-2}$ for somebody weighing 60 kg.

? (Page 81)

The jumper would slow down more quickly at the end.

Chapter 3

? (Page 84)

The spring and particle could move along a smooth horizontal groove.

? (Page 84)

The particle is pulled in towards O by the tension in the spring. When it has passed O it is pushed back again by the thrust in the spring. It oscillates backwards and forwards about O.

? (Page 84)

A sine wave starting at the top of its cycle.

? (Page 85)

$a\sqrt{\dfrac{k}{m}}$ is its speed at O and this is its maximum speed.

? (Page 85)

The acceleration is always directed towards O. When P is moving towards O it speeds up and when it is moving away from O it slows down.

? (Page 85)

$0, 0, \pm a\omega$

Exercise 3A (Page 88)

1 (i) $\ddot{x} = -9x$
    (a) $\pm 6\,\text{cm s}^{-1}, 0$
    (b) $0, 18\,\text{cm s}^{-2}$
    (c) $5.2\,\text{cm s}^{-1}$
 (ii) $\ddot{x} = -100x$
    (a) $\pm 1\,\text{ms}^{-1}, 0$
    (b) $0, 10\,\text{ms}^{-2}$
    (c) $0.87\,\text{ms}^{-1}$

 (iii) $\ddot{x} = -\pi^2 x$
    (a) $\pm a\pi\,\text{ms}^{-1}, 0$
    (b) $0, a\pi^2\,\text{ms}^{-2}$
    (c) $\dfrac{\sqrt{3}}{2}\,a\pi\,\text{ms}^{-1}$

2 2.45 cm above O

3 (i) 10.4 cm
 (ii) $\pm 41.8\,\text{cm s}^{-2}$
 (iii) $20.9\,\text{cm s}^{-1}$
 (iv) $18.3\,\text{cm s}^{-1}$
 (v) 9.04 cm

4 (i) $55\pi, 110\pi, 220\pi, 440\pi,$ below; $1760\pi, 3520\pi,$
    $7040\pi,$ above
 (ii) $22.1\,\text{ms}^{-1}, 0.173\,\text{ms}^{-1}$

5 (i) $4000\pi, 25.1\,\text{ms}^{-1}$
 (ii) $\ddot{x} = -16\,000\,000\pi^2 x, 316\,000\,\text{ms}^{-2}$

6 (i)

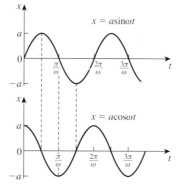

 (ii) 33.3 Hz, 209
 (iii) $73.3\,\text{ms}^{-1}$

7 (i) 1.885, 1.13 m
 (ii) $2.12\,\text{ms}^{-1}$

8 (i) $2.67\,\text{ms}^{-1}$
 (ii) $839\,\text{ms}^{-2}$
 (iii) $1.89\,\text{ms}^{-1}$

9 (i), (iv) and (v) are true

10 (i) $\dfrac{\sqrt{15}}{4}\,a\omega$

  (ii) $\dfrac{\sqrt{3}}{2}\,a$

? (Page 92)

$x = a\cos\omega t, \dot{x} = -a\omega\sin\omega t, \ddot{x} = -a\omega^2\cos\omega t = -\omega^2 x$

They have the same amplitude and period but start at different points in the cycle.

❓ (Page 93)

$\dot{x} = -a\omega\sin\omega t$ then square as in the text with $\sin\omega t$
and $\cos\omega t$ interchanged.

Exercise 3B (Page 95)

1 **(i)** 5 m

(ii) 16 s

(iii) 5, $\dfrac{\pi}{8}$

(iv) **(a)** 0

(b) 1.96 ms^{-1}

(c) 0

2 **(i)** 0.2 s, 0.08 m

(ii) 0.08, 10π

(iii) $-0.8\pi\sin 10\pi t$, 0.08, 0

(iv) 0, -2.51 ms^{-1}, negative direction

3 **(i)** **(a)**

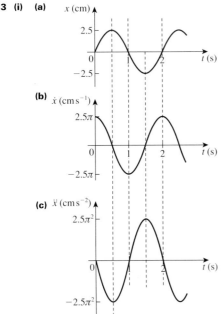

(ii) x and $\ddot{x} = 0$ when $\dot{x}$ has maximum positive
and maximum negative values; x has a
maximum positive and $\ddot{x}$ has a maximum
negative or vice versa when $\dot{x} = 0$

4 **(i)** 2, $\dfrac{\pi}{6}$

(ii) 40 m

(iii) 1.05 ms^{-1}

(iv) $\dfrac{\pi}{3}\cos\dfrac{\pi}{6}t$

(v) 2 s

5 **(i)** 4, 2.5

(ii) $10\cos 4t$

(iii) **(a)** 6.97 cm s^{-1}, positive

(b) -6.54 cm s^{-1}, negative

(iv) **(a)** 1.79 cm

(b) 6.89 cm

6 **(i)**

(ii) $\dfrac{\pi}{6}$, $x = 10\sin\dfrac{\pi}{6}t$

(iii) 5, $5\sqrt{3}$, 10 cm

(iv) 5, 3.66, 1.34 cm; speed is decreasing

(v) e.g. 3rd and 4th seconds, when it covers the
same 'ground' or when its positions are
symmetrical about the centre

7 **(i)** $\dfrac{\pi}{4}$, $x = 10\cos\dfrac{\pi}{4}t$

(ii) $\dot{x} = -\dfrac{5\pi}{2}\sin\dfrac{\pi}{4}t$, 0, -5.55 cm s^{-1}, -7.85 cm s^{-1};

both negative, x decreasing

(iii) the acceleration is not constant

8 **(i)** 20, $\dfrac{\pi}{12}$, $\dot{x} = \dfrac{5\pi}{3}\cos\dfrac{\pi}{12}t$

(ii) **(a)** 0, $\dfrac{5\pi}{3}$

(b) 10, $\dfrac{5\pi\sqrt{3}}{6}$

(iii) 2, 10, $\dfrac{5\pi\sqrt{3}}{6}$, $-\dfrac{5\pi\sqrt{3}}{6}$

9 **(i)** 20, $\dfrac{\pi}{12}$, $\dot{x} = -\dfrac{5\pi}{3}\sin\dfrac{\pi}{12}t$

(ii) **(a)** 20, 0

(b) $10\sqrt{3}$, $-\dfrac{5\pi}{6}$

(iii)

(iv) 10, 14, $-\dfrac{5\pi}{6}$, $\dfrac{5\pi}{6}$

10 **(ii)** 4π ms^{-1}

(iii) $80\pi^2$ ms^{-2}

(iv) $\dfrac{1}{3}$

11 **(i)** 3 m, π s

(ii) 6 ms^{-1}

(iii) $\ddot{y} = -4y$

(iv) 5.45 m (the string is slack when the downward
force necessary for SHM is greater than mg.)

(v) 1.26 s

12 (i)

2, 3

(ii) $x = 4$

(iv) $-5\pi^2\sin\pi t$

(v) SHM; centre, $x = h$; amplitude, a; period, $\dfrac{2\pi}{\omega}$

13 (i) 0.65 m, 0.35 m

(ii) $x = 0.5 + 0.15\sin 2\pi t$ (m)

(iii) (a) 0.05 s

    (b) 0.62 s

14 (i) 355 minutes

(ii) 130 minutes

(iii)

(iv) $\dfrac{2\pi}{365}$ rad per day (approx.)

(v) $355 + 130\cos\left(\dfrac{2\pi(D-1)}{365}\right)$

(vi) 4.55 am

15 (i) 0.05 m, 0.32 seconds

(ii) 0.900 ms^{-1} down, 7.71 ms^{-2} up

(iii)

(iv) $x = 0.05\cos 6.25\pi t$, 0.219 seconds

❓ (Page 103)

All oscillations with the same frequency can be added to form a single oscillation with that frequency.

❓ (Page 105)

(i) $x = a\sin(\omega t - \pi)$ or $-a\sin\omega t$

(ii) $x = a\sin\left(\omega t - \dfrac{\pi}{2}\right)$ or $-a\cos\omega t$

(iii) $x = x_0 + a\cos\omega t$

(iv) $x = x_0 - a\sin\omega t$

Exercise 3C (Page 110)

1 (i) (a)

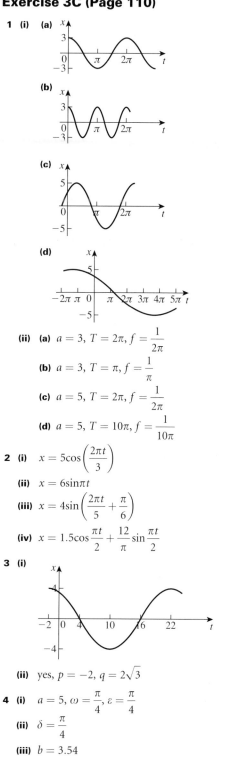

    (b)

    (c)

    (d)

(ii) (a) $a = 3$, $T = 2\pi$, $f = \dfrac{1}{2\pi}$

    (b) $a = 3$, $T = \pi$, $f = \dfrac{1}{\pi}$

    (c) $a = 5$, $T = 2\pi$, $f = \dfrac{1}{2\pi}$

    (d) $a = 5$, $T = 10\pi$, $f = \dfrac{1}{10\pi}$

2 (i) $x = 5\cos\left(\dfrac{2\pi t}{3}\right)$

(ii) $x = 6\sin\pi t$

(iii) $x = 4\sin\left(\dfrac{2\pi t}{5} + \dfrac{\pi}{6}\right)$

(iv) $x = 1.5\cos\dfrac{\pi t}{2} + \dfrac{12}{\pi}\sin\dfrac{\pi t}{2}$

3 (i)

(ii) yes, $p = -2$, $q = 2\sqrt{3}$

4 (i) $a = 5$, $\omega = \dfrac{\pi}{4}$, $\varepsilon = \dfrac{\pi}{4}$

(ii) $\delta = \dfrac{\pi}{4}$

(iii) $b = 3.54$

5 (i)

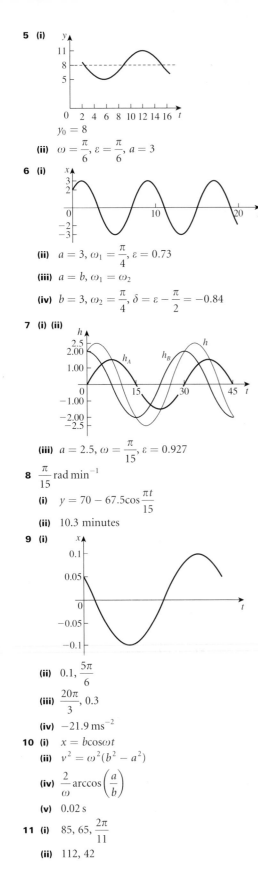

$y_0 = 8$

(ii) $\omega = \dfrac{\pi}{6}, \varepsilon = \dfrac{\pi}{6}, a = 3$

6 (i)

(ii) $a = 3, \omega_1 = \dfrac{\pi}{4}, \varepsilon = 0.73$

(iii) $a = b, \omega_1 = \omega_2$

(iv) $b = 3, \omega_2 = \dfrac{\pi}{4}, \delta = \varepsilon - \dfrac{\pi}{2} = -0.84$

7 (i) (ii)

(iii) $a = 2.5, \omega = \dfrac{\pi}{15}, \varepsilon = 0.927$

8 $\dfrac{\pi}{15}$ rad min^{-1}

(i) $y = 70 - 67.5\cos\dfrac{\pi t}{15}$

(ii) 10.3 minutes

9 (i)

(ii) $0.1, \dfrac{5\pi}{6}$

(iii) $\dfrac{20\pi}{3}, 0.3$

(iv) $-21.9\,\text{ms}^{-2}$

10 (i) $x = b\cos\omega t$

(ii) $v^2 = \omega^2(b^2 - a^2)$

(iv) $\dfrac{2}{\omega}\arccos\left(\dfrac{a}{b}\right)$

(v) 0.02 s

11 (i) $85, 65, \dfrac{2\pi}{11}$

(ii) 112, 42

12 (i) SHM; mean, h_0; amplitude, a; period, $\dfrac{2\pi}{\omega}$

(ii) $6, 4, \dfrac{\pi}{6}, \dfrac{\pi}{6}$

(iii) $0.647\,\text{m h}^{-1}, 1.043\,\text{m h}^{-2}$

(iv) $2.094\,\text{m h}^{-1}$

13 (i) 0.0598 s, 0.5

(ii) $\beta = 1.5 + 1.5\sin\left(\dfrac{\pi}{3}t\right)$

❓ (Page 117)

(i) < 0.173 rad ($\approx 10°$)

(ii) < 0.244 rad ($\approx 14°$)

(iii) < 0.344 rad ($\approx 20°$)

❓ (Page 122)

Yes, g cancels out.

Exercise 3D (Page 124)

1 (i)

(ii) $0.15\ddot{\theta} = -0.3g\sin\theta$

(iii) θ small so that $\sin\theta \approx \theta$

(iv) $\ddot{\theta} = -2g\theta$; 1.42 s

(v) No

2 (i) 0.0873 rad

(ii) 3.48 s

(iii) $a = 0.0873, \omega = 1.807, \varepsilon = 0$

(iv) $0.473\,\text{ms}^{-1}, 0.095\,\text{Ns}$

3 (i) 0.993 m

(ii) (a) none

(b) multiplies by $\sqrt{2}$

(c) none

(d) multiplies by $\sqrt{8}$

4 (i) $\ddot{\theta} = -\dfrac{g}{4}\theta$; stone is a particle, no air resistance, θ is small

(ii) 4.01 s

5 (ii) $x = 0.25\sin 4\pi t$

(iii) $v^2 = \pi^2(1 - 16x^2)$

(iv)

$R - mg = m\ddot{x}$

The contact force, R, must be $\geqslant 0$

(v) $0.312\,\text{m}$, $3.04\,\text{ms}^{-1}$

(vi) $0.145\,\text{s}$

6 (i) bouyancy = weight, $k = \dfrac{mg}{l}$

(ii) $F = \dfrac{mg}{l}(x+l)$, $\ddot{x} = -\dfrac{g}{l}x$

7 (ii) $x = 0.2$, $\dot{x} = 0$ when $t = 0$

(iv) $a = 0.2$, $f = 0.356$

(v) $0.447\,\text{ms}^{-1}$

8 (ii) $\ddot{x} = -600x$

(iii) $t = 0$, $x = -0.02$

(iv) $x = 0.02\cos(\sqrt{600}\,t + \pi)$

(v) $3.90\,\text{Hz}$

(vi) $0.49\,\text{ms}^{-1}$, $12\,\text{ms}^{-2}$

9 (i) $\dfrac{15l}{4}$

(ii) $\dfrac{\lambda}{4}$

(iii) $\ddot{x} = -\dfrac{4\lambda}{3lm}x$

Initial conditions: $x = 0$, $v = \dfrac{\mu}{m}$

(iv) $a = \mu\sqrt{\dfrac{3l}{4\lambda m}}$, $f = \sqrt{\dfrac{\lambda}{3lm}} \times \dfrac{1}{\pi}$

(v) $x = \mu\sqrt{\dfrac{3l}{4\lambda m}}\sin\left(\sqrt{\dfrac{4\lambda}{3lm}}\,t\right)$

10 (i) $0.025\,\text{m}$

(ii) $7.5 + 300x\,\text{N}$

(iv) $x = 0.02\cos(20t)$

(v) $3\,\text{cm} > 0.025\,\text{m}$ so string is not in tension throughout

11 (ii)

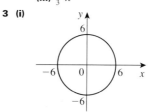

$mg - T = m\ddot{x}$

(iii) $\ddot{x} = -\dfrac{k}{m}x$

(iv) $\dfrac{mg}{k}$

12 (i) $l_0 + \dfrac{mgl_0}{2\lambda}$ below the ceiling, $2l_0 + \dfrac{2mgl_0}{\lambda}$ below the ceiling.

(ii) $\ddot{x} = \dfrac{-2\lambda x}{ml_0}$, $\ddot{x} = -\dfrac{\lambda x}{2ml_0}$

(iii) $\pi\sqrt{\dfrac{2ml_0}{\lambda}}$, $2\pi\sqrt{\dfrac{2ml_0}{\lambda}}$

13 (i) (a) $2.1\,\text{ms}^{-1}$

(b) $0.87\,\text{m}$

(c) $0.022\,\text{N}$

(ii) $3\,\text{s}$

14 (i) $10g\,\text{Nm}^{-1}$

(ii) $x = 2\cos\sqrt{g}\,t$

(iii) $0.669\,\text{s}$

(iv) $5.42\,\text{ms}^{-1}$

(v) $2.4\,\text{s}$

15 (i) $0.000\,245\,\text{m}$

(ii) $0.003\,185\,\text{m}$

(iii) 3

(iv) $\ddot{y} = -40\,000y$, $0.588\,\text{ms}^{-1}$

Chapter 4

Exercise 4A (Page 139)

1 (a) For sketches see Exercise 4B question 1

(b) (i) $\dfrac{104}{3}\pi$

(ii) 8π

(iii) $\dfrac{652}{3}\pi$

(iv) $\dfrac{2}{3}\pi$

(v) $\dfrac{9}{2}\pi(e^3 - 1)$

(vi) $\dfrac{\pi^2}{4}$

2 (a) For sketches see Exercise 4B question 2

(b) (i) $\dfrac{96}{5}\pi$

(ii) 18π

(iii) $\dfrac{28}{3}\pi$

3 (i)

(ii) 0.235 litres

4 (i)

(ii) 45 litres

5 (i) $y = \dfrac{rx}{h}$

6 (i)

Answers

(ii)

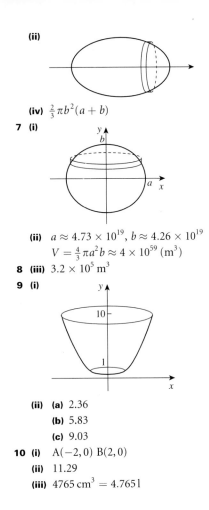

(iv) $\frac{2}{3}\pi b^2(a+b)$

7 (i)

(ii) $a \approx 4.73 \times 10^{19}$, $b \approx 4.26 \times 10^{19}$
$V = \frac{4}{3}\pi a^2 b \approx 4 \times 10^{59}$ (m^3)

8 (iii) 3.2×10^5 m^3

9 (i)

(ii) (a) 2.36

(b) 5.83

(c) 9.03

10 (i) A$(-2, 0)$ B$(2, 0)$

(ii) 11.29

(iii) $4765 \text{ cm}^3 = 4.765\text{l}$

Exercise 4B (Page 151)

1 (i) (a)

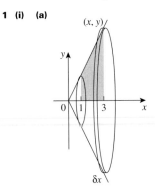

(b) $(2.31, 0)$

(ii) (a)

(b) $(2.67, 0)$

(iii) (a)

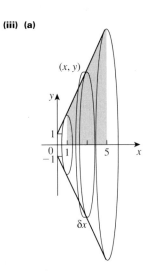

(b) $(3.69, 0)$

(iv) (a)

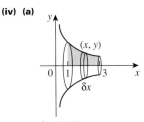

(b) $(1.65, 0)$

(v) (a)

(b) $(1.08, 0)$

(vi) (a)

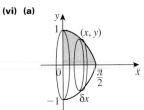

(b) $(0.47, 0)$

2 (i) (a)

(b) $(0, 5)$

200

(ii) (a)

(b) $(0, 3.5)$

(iii) (a)

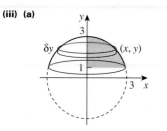

(b) $(0, 1.71)$

3 (i)

(ii) $\frac{128}{105}\pi$

(iii) $(1.25, 0)$

4 (i)

(ii) $v = 30\pi, (2.8, 0)$

(iii) (a) $2, 4$

    (b) $\dfrac{62\pi}{5}$

    (c) $(0, 3.39)$

5 (i)

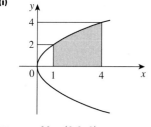

(ii) $V = 8\pi, (1.125, 0)$

6 3.9 cm

---

7 (i)

	Clown	Cone	Hemisphere
Mass	$\frac{1}{3}\pi r^2 \rho (2r + h)$	$\frac{1}{3}\pi r^2 h\rho$	$\frac{2}{3}\pi r^3 \rho$
Dist. of c.o.m. above O	$\bar{y}$	$\frac{1}{4}h$	$-\frac{3}{8}r$

(ii) $\left(\frac{2}{3}r + \frac{1}{3}h\right)\bar{y} = \frac{1}{3}h \times \frac{1}{4}h - \frac{2}{3}r \times \frac{3}{8}r$

(iii) $\sqrt{3}:1$

(iv) upright

8 (i) Using σ as mass per unit area:

	Whole container	Cylinder base	Cylinder walls	Cone
Mass	$132\pi\sigma$	$9\pi\sigma$	$108\pi\sigma$	$15\pi\sigma$
Dist. of c.o.m. above O	$\bar{y}$	0	9	$19\frac{1}{3}$

(ii) 9.56 cm

(iii) 0.30 rad, 17.42°

(iv) The centre of mass will be lower so it is less likely to topple.

9 (i)

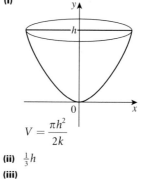

$$V = \frac{\pi h^2}{2k}$$

(ii) $\frac{1}{3}h$

(iii)

	Solid block	Glass	Part removed
Mass	$\dfrac{9^2\pi}{2k}\rho$	$\dfrac{\pi}{2k}(9^2 - 8.8^2)\rho$	$\dfrac{8.8^2\pi}{2k}\rho$
Dist. of c.o.m. below rim	$\frac{1}{3} \times 9$	d	$\frac{1}{3} \times 8.8$

(iv) 7.3 cm

(v) 0.39 rad, 22.4°

10 (iii) $1 - 4\varepsilon$

Chapter 4

201

11 (i) $V = \int_{-1}^{0} 4\pi(1 - 2x^2 + x^4)\,dx$

$= 4\pi\left[x - \dfrac{2x^3}{3} + \dfrac{x^5}{5}\right]_{-1}^{0} = \dfrac{32\pi}{15}$

$\int_{-1}^{0} 4\pi x(1 - 2x^2 + x^4)\,dx$

$= 4\pi\left[\dfrac{x^2}{2} - \dfrac{2x^4}{4} + \dfrac{x^6}{6}\right]_{-1}^{0} = \dfrac{-2\pi}{3}$

$\bar{x} = \dfrac{\dfrac{-2\pi}{3}}{\dfrac{32\pi}{15}} = -\dfrac{5}{16}$

(ii) $\dfrac{\dfrac{32\pi}{15}\left(-\dfrac{5}{16}\right) + \dfrac{1}{3}\pi \times 4k\left(\dfrac{k}{4}\right)}{\dfrac{32\pi}{15} + \dfrac{1}{3}\pi \times 4k}$

$= \dfrac{5(k^2 - 2)}{4(8 + 5k)}$

(iii) (a)

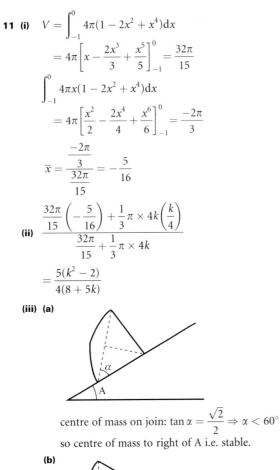

centre of mass on join: $\tan\alpha = \dfrac{\sqrt{2}}{2} \Rightarrow \alpha < 60°$

so centre of mass to right of A i.e. stable.

(b)

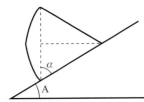

$\alpha = 60°$ so join vertical: centre of mass to right of join so centre of mass to right of A i.e. stable

❓ Activity (Page 156)

About 8:11, see Example 4.7.

Exercise 4C (Page 160)

1 (i) (a) $\bar{x} = 0$

(b)

(c) $(4 - x^2)\delta x$

(d) $(0, 1.6)$

(ii) (a) $\bar{y} = 0$

(b)

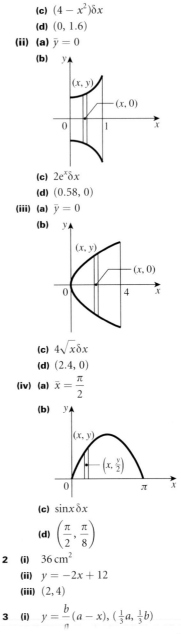

(c) $2e^x\delta x$

(d) $(0.58, 0)$

(iii) (a) $\bar{y} = 0$

(b)

(c) $4\sqrt{x}\,\delta x$

(d) $(2.4, 0)$

(iv) (a) $\bar{x} = \dfrac{\pi}{2}$

(b)

(c) $\sin x\,\delta x$

(d) $\left(\dfrac{\pi}{2}, \dfrac{\pi}{8}\right)$

2 (i) $36\,\text{cm}^2$

(ii) $y = -2x + 12$

(iii) $(2, 4)$

3 (i) $y = \dfrac{b}{a}(a - x)$, $\left(\tfrac{1}{3}a, \tfrac{1}{3}b\right)$

(ii) Centre of each strip is on PP′

(iii) G_1 and G_2 are both $\tfrac{1}{3}$PD from QR so G_1G_2 is parallel to QR. G lies on G_1G_2 and PH:HD $= 2:1$ so PG:GP′ $= 2:1$.

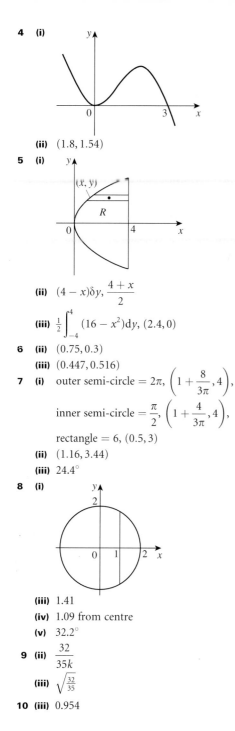

4 (i)

(ii) $(1.8, 1.54)$

5 (i)

(ii) $(4 - x)\delta y, \dfrac{4 + x}{2}$

(iii) $\dfrac{1}{2}\displaystyle\int_{-4}^{4} (16 - x^2)\mathrm{d}y, (2.4, 0)$

6 (ii) $(0.75, 0.3)$

(iii) $(0.447, 0.516)$

7 (i) outer semi-circle $= 2\pi, \left(1 + \dfrac{8}{3\pi}, 4\right)$,

inner semi-circle $= \dfrac{\pi}{2}, \left(1 + \dfrac{4}{3\pi}, 4\right)$,

rectangle $= 6, (0.5, 3)$

(ii) $(1.16, 3.44)$

(iii) $24.4°$

8 (i)

(iii) 1.41

(iv) 1.09 from centre

(v) $32.2°$

9 (ii) $\dfrac{32}{35k}$

(iii) $\sqrt{\dfrac{32}{35}}$

10 (iii) 0.954

Chapter 5

❷ (Page 169)

Examples include $lbh, \pi r^2 h, x^3, \frac{4}{3}\pi r^3$

Exercise 5A (Page 172)

See page 205.

Exercise 5B (Page 176)

1 (i) All L^2T^{-2}; consistent

(ii) All L; consistent

(iii) All MLT^{-2}; consistent

(iv) L.H.S. MLT^{-2}, R.H.S. ML^2T^{-2}; inconsistent

(v) L.H.S. ML^2T^{-2}, R.H.S. MLT^{-1}; inconsistent

(vi) All MLT^{-2}; consistent

(vii) L.H.S. ML^2T^{-2}, R.H.S. MLT^{-2}; inconsistent

(viii) All ML^2T^{-2}; consistent

(ix) Two terms L^2T^{-2} but $[x^2] = L^2$; inconsistent

(x) L.H.S. ML^2T^{-3}, R.H.S. L^2T^{-3}; inconsistent

2 (i) $[v] = LT^{-1}, [h] = L, [\rho] = ML^{-3}, [g] = LT^{-2}$

(ii) $\alpha = \frac{1}{2}, \beta = 0, \gamma = \frac{1}{2}, v = k\sqrt{hg}$

(iii) Deep water

(iv) No difference

3 (i) $t = kd^\alpha g^\beta$

(ii) $t = k\sqrt{\dfrac{d}{g}}$

(iii) $k = 150$

(iv) 36.7 s

4 (i) ML^2T^{-2}

(ii) $E = km^\alpha r^\beta \omega^\gamma$

(iii) $E = kmr^2\omega^2$

(iv) $E = \frac{1}{2}mr^2\omega^2$

(v) 5184 J

5 (i) $e = \dfrac{\text{velocity}}{\text{velocity}}$

(ii) $\alpha = 2, \beta = 0, \gamma = -1, h = \dfrac{kv^2}{g}$

(iii) h is independent of m so both bounce to the same height

(iv) because e is dimensionless and is included in k

(v) $h = \dfrac{e^2 v^2}{2g}$

(vi) $k = \dfrac{e^2}{2}$ is dimensionless

6 (i) $M^{-1}L^3T^{-2}$

(ii) $t = k\sqrt{\dfrac{r_0{}^3}{Gm}}$

(iii) Yes

(iv) $t = \dfrac{k'}{\sqrt{G\rho_0}}$

7 (ii) $x + y = 3$

(iii) $R = 6.72 \times 10^6 \times \dfrac{r^4}{a}$

(iv) 0.213 m^3 s^{-1}

8 (i) $V = \dfrac{kmg}{r\eta}$

(ii) $m = \frac{4}{3}\pi r^3 \rho$

(iii) $V = \dfrac{k_1 r^2 \rho g}{\eta}$

(iv) 0.113 cm

9 **(i)** π is the circumference of a circle divided by its diameter; dimensionless

(ii) $M^{-1}L^3T^{-2}$

(iii) 1.8×10^9

(iv) π (dimensionless) is independent of units, G (not dimensionless) is dependent on its units

10 **(i)** $f = \dfrac{k}{l}\sqrt{\dfrac{T}{m}}$

(ii) $f = \dfrac{1}{2l}\sqrt{\dfrac{T}{m}}$

(iii) 316.2 cycles s^{-1}

11 **(iii)** MT^{-1}

(iv) Dimensionless

(v) $\varepsilon = \dfrac{kcu}{mg}$, $R = R_M\left(1 - \dfrac{kcu}{mg}\right)$

12 **(ii)** $ML^{-1}T^{-2}$, ML^{-3}

(iii) $\alpha = -1$, $\beta = \frac{1}{2}$, $\gamma = -\frac{1}{2}$; by experiment or analysis

(iv) 1.2

(v) much greater; $A \propto \rho c^2$ and $c_{\text{water}} \gg c_{\text{air}}$, $\rho_{\text{water}} \gg \rho_{\text{air}}$

13 **(i)** $0, \frac{1}{2}, -\frac{1}{2}$

(ii) It has the same dimensional quantities so it has the same form of equation.

(iii) $\dfrac{g}{l\cos\theta}$, $\omega^2 > \dfrac{g}{l}$

(iv) $k_2 = 2\pi\sqrt{\cos\theta}$

The simple pendulum has the longer period because $\cos\theta < 1 \Rightarrow k_2 < k_1$.

14 **(i)** $[\text{density}] = ML^{-3}$

$[\text{angular velocity}] = T^{-1}$

e.g. $[\text{power}] = [\text{force}][\text{velocity}]$

$= MLT^{-2} \times LT^{-1}$

$= ML^2 \times T^{-3}$

(ii) $ML^2T^{-3} = L^\alpha \times T^{-\beta} \times M^\gamma L^{-3\gamma}$

$\gamma = 1$

$-\beta = -3 \quad \Rightarrow \beta = 3$

$\alpha - 3\gamma = 2 \quad \Rightarrow \alpha = 5$

(iii) $[\eta] = [\omega\rho d^2]$

$= T^{-1} \times ML^{-3} \times L^2$

$= ML^{-1}T^{-1}$

Cannot calculate δ as 4 variables and only 3 equations from M, L and T. (or value of δ does not affect dimensional consistency as $\dfrac{\omega\rho d^2}{\eta}$ is dimensionless)

(iv) $\dfrac{\omega \times 1000 \times 0.6^2}{0.001} = \dfrac{25 \times 850 \times 1.8^2}{0.012}$

$\omega = 15.9375$

(v) $\dfrac{P}{3} = \left(\dfrac{1.8}{0.6}\right)^5 \left(\dfrac{25}{15.9375}\right)^3 \left(\dfrac{850}{1000}\right)$

$P = 2400\,\text{kW}$ (2 s.f.)

15 **(ii)** $25\,\text{N}$

(iii) 0.75

(iv) $0.668{:}1$

Exercise 5A (Page 172)

Quantity	Formula	Dimensions	S.I. unit
Area	$l \times w$	L^2	m^2
Volume	$l \times w \times h$	L^3	m^3
Speed	$\dfrac{d}{t}$	LT^{-1}	ms^{-1}
Acceleration	$\dfrac{v}{t}$	LT^{-2}	ms^{-2}
g	acceleration	LT^{-2}	ms^{-2}
Force	$F = ma$	MLT^{-2}	N, newton
Weight	mg	MLT^{-2}	N, newton
Kinetic energy	$\frac{1}{2}mv^2$	ML^2T^{-2}	J, joule
Gravitational potential energy	mgh	ML^2T^{-2}	J, joule
Work	Fs	ML^2T^{-2}	J, joule
Power	Fv	ML^2T^{-3}	W, watt
Impulse	Ft	MLT^{-1}	Ns
Momentum	mV	MLT^{-1}	Ns
Pressure	$\dfrac{Force}{Area}$	$ML^{-1}T^{-2}$	Nm^{-2}, pascal
Density	$\dfrac{m}{V}$	ML^{-3}	$kg\,m^{-3}$
Moment	Fd	ML^2T^{-2}	Nm
Angle	$s = r\theta$	Dimensionless	(radian)
Angular velocity	$\dfrac{Angle}{Time}$	T^{-1}	$rad\,s^{-1}$
Angular acceleration	$\dfrac{Angular\ velocity}{Time}$	T^{-2}	$rad\,s^{-2}$
Modulus of elasticity	$T = \dfrac{\lambda x}{l_0}$	MLT^{-2}	N
Stiffness	$T = kx$	MT^{-2}	Nm^{-1}
Gravitational constant, G	$F = \dfrac{Gm_1 m_2}{d^2}$	$M^{-1}L^3T^{-2}$	$Nm^2\,kg^{-2}$
Period	Time interval	T	s
Frequency	$\dfrac{1}{Period}$	T^{-1}	Hz, hertz
Coefficient of restitution	$\dfrac{V\ separation}{V\ approach}$	Dimensionless	—
Coefficient of friction	$F = \mu R$	Dimensionless	—

Index